THE CRICKET
QUIZ BOOK

THE CRICKET QUIZ BOOK

Compiled by Adam Pearson, Alan Finch and Chris Cowlin

Foreword by Dickie Bird MBE

APEX PUBLISHING LTD

First published in 2008 by
Apex Publishing Ltd
PO Box 7086, Clacton on Sea, Essex, CO15 5WN, England
www.apexpublishing.co.uk

British Library Cataloguing-in-Publication Data
A catalogue record for this book
is available from the British Library

ISBN HARDBACK: 1-906358-00-1   978-1-906358-00-6

Typeset in 10.5pt Chianti Bdlt Win95BT

Cover Design: Siobhan Smith

Printed and bound in Great Britain by
Biddles Ltd., King's Lynn, Norfolk

Author's Note:
Please can you contact me: **ChrisCowlin@btconnect.com** if you find any mistakes/errors in this book as I would like to put them right on any future reprints of this book. I would also like to hear from cricket fans who have enjoyed the test! For more information on me and my books please look at: **www.ChrisCowlin.com**

We would like to dedicate this book to:

Dickie Bird - a true Cricket legend!

FOREWORD

I was brought up to believe that having respect for others is the greatest virtue of all. I have tried to live my life with this in mind and it has served me well. People I have met from all walks of life - sporting greats to kids on the park alike - have gone out of their way to return the compliment and this has made me the person I am today. It has also resulted in a number of close friendships that I still hold very dear. My career in cricket has spanned many years, both as a player and then as an umpire, where I was fortunate enough to achieve every honour the game had to offer; of this I am immensely proud. From the playing fields of Barnsley to international cricket shrines across the world, my love of sport in general and cricket in particular has never faded. Reflecting on my career in cricket, people often ask, "What is your proudest moment?" to which I always reply, "I am proud never to have forgotten my roots." My parents struggled to give me the best they could afford and for that I will always be grateful. When I retired from umpiring, I decided that I wanted to use my position in the public eye to give something back and to help those young people who were in the financially disadvantaged position I had found myself. In my view, every child - regardless of their circumstances - should have the opportunity to take part in the sport of their choice, to get themselves fit and get away from the street corners and television. The Dickie Bird Foundation was therefore launched in 2004 and has since become the biggest part of my life. With a small number of trustees, we are now going from strength to strength. The Foundation offers grants to help financially disadvantaged children take part in their chosen sport. These have ranged from horse riding, ice skating, karate and athletics to football, rugby and cricket - there have been many more. Turning to this book, I would like to express my heartfelt thanks to the publishers for their significant support for my Foundation.

As you might imagine, I am often asked questions about the laws of cricket, the players, the clubs and everything else to do with the game. This quiz book will hopefully leave you with the feeling that you have learned something new, recalled things you had forgotten - and then quickly forgotten them again. You may be of expert standard and be able to answer all the questions. You may be a bar room bore who knows nothing about everything. You could even be the next Dickie Bird: someone who has a lifetime of cricketing knowledge - but still sometimes manages to forget the most famous players' names. I hope you enjoy the book and remember, by purchasing this, you too are doing your bit to help financially disadvantaged children.

Best Wishes
Dickie Bird MBE

INTRODUCTION

I would first of all like to thank Dickie Bird for writing the foreword to this book. Dickie is a true cricket legend and I am very grateful for his help on this project.

I am honoured to donate £1 from each book sale to Dickie's 'The Dickie Bird Foundation Charity'. It is a registered charity - **www.thedickiebirdfoundation.org** - and the foundation was established by Dickie in March 2004, with the aim of helping disadvantaged young people, nationwide, to participate in sport.

I would like to thank the Grants Officer of The Dickie Bird Foundation, Les Smith, for his support in creating this book. It has been great working with Adam Pearson again, as we have worked together on a few football titles (see the back of this book), and working with Alan Finch in compiling this publication has been a lot of fun.

I hope you enjoy this book. Hopefully it should bring back some wonderful memories whatever team or country you follow! In closing, I would like to thank all my friends and family for encouraging me to complete this project.

Best wishes
Chris Cowlin

DICKIE BIRD

1. What is Dickie Bird's full name?

2. Where in Yorkshire was Dickie Bird born?

3. Which County Cricket Club did Dickie Bird first play for other than Yorkshire?

4. In what year did Dickie Bird play his last first class match?

5. In what year did Dickie Bird umpire his first Test match?

6. In Dickie Bird's final Test match the two teams formed a 'guard of honour' as he came out onto the field of play. Which two teams were involved?

7. Who wrote the foreword in Dickie Bird's book *My Autobiography*?

8. Dickie Bird was awarded what honour by Her Majesty the Queen in 1986?

9. In what year was Dickie Bird born?

10. Dickie Bird umpired how many World Cup finals?

GROUNDS

11.   At which Test Cricket ground is the Football Stand End?

12.   At which Test Cricket ground is the City End?

13.   At which Test Cricket ground is the Brian Statham End?

14.   At which Test Cricket ground is the Lumley End?

15.   Glamorgan's Cardiff home is called what?

16.   At which County Cricket ground is the Nackington Road End?

17.   At which County Cricket/ODI ground is the Northern End?

18.   At which County Cricket ground is the Bennett End?

19.   At which County Cricket ground is the Sea End?

20.   Essex's Ilford ground is called what?

BRIAN LARA

21.   *What is Brian Lara's nickname?*

22.   *In what year was Brian Lara born?*

23.   *In what year did Brian Lara make his Test debut?*

24.   *For which English County Cricket club did Brian Lara play?*

25.   *For which West Indies cricket club did Brian Lara play between 1987 and 2006?*

26.   *What was Brian Lara's ODI shirt number?*

27.   *Against which nation did Brian Lara make his final Test appearance?*

28.   *Brian Lara's last international match was against England on 21 April 2007. Who ran him out?*

29.   *In July 2007 Brian Lara signed for which Indian Cricket League club?*

30.   *Brian Lara struck 277 in his maiden Test Century against which nation?*

NICKNAMES

Match up the player with his nickname

31.	Phil Tufnell	KP
32.	Harold Bird	Athers
33.	Shaun Udal	Blowers
34.	Andrew Flintoff	Beefy
35.	Kevin Pietersen	Nass
36.	Ian Botham	The Cat
37.	Graham Gooch	Shaggy
38.	Henry Blofield	Freddie
39.	Michael Atherton	Zap
40.	Nassar Hussain	Dickie

THE WETHERALL AWARD

Match up the year with the Wetherall Award winner

41.	2004	*Phil Simmons (Leicestershire)*
42.	2002	*Gavin Hamilton (Yorkshire)*
43.	2000	*Franklyn Stephenson (Nottinghamshire)*
44.	1998	*Chris Lewis (Nottinghamshire)*
45.	1996	*Malcolm Marshall (Hampshire)*
46.	1994	*Darren Maddy (Leicestershire)*
47.	1992	*Robert Croft (Glamorgan)*
48.	1990	*Richard Hadlee (Nottinghamshire)*
49.	1988	*Martin Bicknell (Surrey)*
50.	1986	*Franklyn Stephenson (Sussex)*

MIKE ATHERTON

51.   In what year was Mike Atherton born?

52.   For which club did Mike Atherton play between 1987 and 2001?

53.   Mike Atherton is known by four nicknames - Athers, FEC, Dread and what else?

54.   Against which nation did Mike Atherton make his Test debut?

55.   In what year did Mike Atherton make his Test debut?

56.   What bowling style did Mike Atherton adopt?

57.   Against which nation did Mike Atherton make his ODI debut?

58.   In what year did Mike Atherton make his last Test appearance?

59.   Which part of Mike Atherton's body was affected by a degenerative condition that first appeared in 1991?

60.   What is the name of Mike Atherton's 2002 autobiography?

ONE DAY INTERNATIONALS - 1

61.   How many overs per innings are generally played in One Day Internationals?

62.   In what year was the first One Day International played?

63.   Which two nations contested the first One Day International?

64.   As of 2007, Australia had won the most One Day Internationals, but which nation is second in the list?

65.   How many consecutive One Day International wins did Australia achieve between 11 January 2003 and 24 May 2003?

66.   Which nation holds the record for the most consecutive One Day International defeats (23 between 8 October 1999 and 9 October 2002)?

67.   In 2006 the Netherlands were on the receiving end of the biggest One Day International innings score in history. Which nation scored 443 for 9 against them?

68.   Which Pakistan batsman holds the record for the highest innings score in a One Day International?

69.   Which bowler finished his career with a total of 502 One Day International wickets between 1984 and 2003?

70.   Who was the Sri Lanka bowler that finished a One Day International match against Zimbabwe with 8 wickets for 19 runs in 2001/02?

ESSEX

71. Which batsman scored 30,701 runs for Essex between 1973 and 1997?

72. In what year was Essex County Cricket Club founded - A: 1846; B: 1856; C: 1866; or D: 1876?

73. By what name is Essex known in the One Day game?

74. Where does Essex play most of its home games?

75. Which player took 1,610 wickets for Essex during his career?

76. In what year did Essex first win the County Championship?

77. Who became Essex captain in 2007?

78. In what year did Ronnie Irani join Essex?

79. In what year did Graham Gooch first become captain of Essex?

80. Who was Essex's Pakistani player in 2007?

SHANE WARNE

81. What is Shane Warne's full name?

82. For which Australian club did Shane Warne play from 1990 until 2007?

83. In what year did Shane Warne make his Test debut?

84. Which Englishman was Shane Warne's 700th Test wicket?

85. In what year was Shane Warne made captain of Hampshire CCC?

86. Who overtook Shane Warne as the greatest wicket taker of all time in 2007?

87. Which Indian batsman was Shane Warne's first Test wicket?

88. What was Shane Warne's shirt number in One Day cricket?

89. What was Shane Warne's bowling style?

90. Which English batsman was Shane Warne's 150th, 250th and 400th Test wickets?

TEST CRICKET - 1

91.   In what year was the first official Test match played?

92.   Which were the first three nations to attain Test status?

93.   Name all ten Test status nations as of 2007.

94.   In what year was South Africa suspended from Test cricket?

95.   In what decade did the West Indies become a Test status nation?

96.   How many ties have there been in the history of Test cricket - A: 0; B: 1; C: 2; or D: 3. (A tie in cricket is when both teams are bowled out and have finished with the exact same score, as opposed to a draw in which a match has not been able to be completed).

97.   At which Test cricket ground is the Nursery End?

98.   After how many overs in a Test match is the bowling team given the option to take a new ball?

99.   Which nation holds the record for the most consecutive Test match draws (10 in total)?

100.   Which nation holds the record for the highest innings score in Test cricket (903/7)?

GRAHAM GOOCH

101.   In what year was Graham Gooch awarded the OBE?

102.   In what year did Graham Gooch make his Test debut?

103.   What is Graham Gooch's middle name?

104.   For which South African club did Graham Gooch play?

105.   In what year did Graham Gooch play his last Test match?

106.   Where in London was Graham Gooch born?

107.   In what year did Graham Gooch take part in a tour of South Africa that resulted in a three year ban?

108.   In what year was Graham Gooch first appointed England captain?

109.   Against which nation did Graham Gooch make his ODI debut in 1976?

110.   How many Test wickets did Graham Gooch take - A: 3; B: 13; C: 23; or D: 33?

AUSTRALIA

111. Who became coach of the Australian cricket team in February 2007?

112. Who was Ricky Ponting's vice captain in 2007?

113. Which Australian faced the first ball and scored the first runs in Test cricket - A: Charles Bannerman; B: Arthur Marsh; C: Bruce Smith; or D: William May?

114. As of 2007, who had appeared in the most Tests for Australia?

115. Australia's largest victory in a Test match was in Februay 2002, with an innings of 360 runs against which nation?

116. As of 2007 who had scored the most Test runs for Australia?

117. Who set a record for the highest individual score in a Test match for Australia when he scored 380 against Zimbabwe in October 2003?

118. Who holds the record for the most ducks by an Australian (35 in 138 innings) as of 2007?

119. Who holds the record for the most catches in a career by an Australian?

120. What is the title of the song sung by the Australian team after every victory?

CRICKET RULES

121. What are the four things that a substitute in cricket is not permitted to do in a game?

122. How many centimetres must a cricket ball be in diameter?

123. How long (in yards) is the cricket 'pitch'?

124. How tall, in inches, must a cricket stump be?

125. When does the ball cease to be 'dead'?

126. How many minutes does the replacement batsman have to take the crease after his predecessor is dismissed before he is timed out?

127. Match referees are used at what level of cricket?

128. Explain what is scored by the batting team if the bowling team declares 'ball lost'?

129. Are byes credited to the batsman's score or just the batting team's score?

130. Can an umpire penalise the bowling team by disregarding a valid excessive appeal by a bowler?

ALEC STEWART

131.   In what year was Alec Stewart born?

132.   For which club did Alec Stewart play?

133.   Of what Premiership football club is Alec Stewart a well-known supporter?

134.   Which England and Surrey player was married to Alec Stewart's sister Judy?

135.   In what year was Alec Stewart named as the Wisden Cricketer of the Year?

136.   Against which nation in 1994 did Alec Stewart score centuries in both innings of a Test match?

137.   Alec Stewart's highest Test score was 190 against which nation in 1992?

138.   In what year was Alec Stewart awarded the MBE?

139.   How many first class wickets did Alec Stewart get in his career while bowling - A: 0; B: 1; C: 2; or D: 3?

140.   Alec Stewart is the son of which former English Test cricketer?

MUTTIAH MURALITHARAN

141. In what year was Muttiah Muralitharan born?

142. What is Muttiah Muralitharan's bowling style?

143. Which Australian batsman was Muttiah Muralitharan's first Test wicket in 1992?

144. Which Bangladesh batsman was Muttiah Muralitharan's 550th and 600th Test wickets?

145. For which County Cricket Club did Muttiah Muralitharan play between 1999 and 2007?

146. Against which nation did Muttiah Muralitharan get his highest Test batting score of 67?

147. For what native club did Muttiah Muralitharan begin playing in 1991/92?

148. Which Englishman was Muttiah Muralitharan's record breaking 709th Test wicket?

149. Which tragic English batsman was Muttiah Muralitharan's 200th Test wicket?

150. Where in Sri Lanka was Muttiah Muralitharan born?

UMPIRES

151. Who is the West Indies umpire that has umpired over 120 Test matches from 1989?

152. What is the name of the Pakistani umpire that England captain Mike Gatting argued with in 1987?

153. Who was the umpire that was famous for lifting one foot off of the ground whenever the score reached 111?

154. Name the Australian umpire who was banned from top level matches in 2006 after his conduct during a Test match between England and Pakistan.

155. Name the English umpire who officiated at 36 Test matches between 1971 and 1988.

156. Name the Sri Lankan umpire who has officiated at over 30 Test matches since 2000.

157. Who is the South African that has umpired over 80 Test matches since 1992?

158. Name the Indian who umpired 73 Test matches between 1993 and 2004.

159. Name the former England Test cricketer who went on to umpire 25 Test matches between 1996 and 2003.

160. Who was the West Indian umpire that was involved in the England versus Pakistan ball tampering scandal in 2006?

ENGLAND

161. What other country does the England cricket team represent?

162. Who replaced Duncan Fletcher as head coach of England in 2007?

163. How many times has England finished as runner-up in the Cricket World Cup?

164. Who is the player that holds the record for the highest individual score in a match for England (364 in 1938 versus Australia at the Oval)?

165. Three players share the record for the most centuries for England (22 in total). Name two of them.

166. Who is the legendary player that scored the first England century?

167. Which England fielder has been involved in the most dismissals (277)?

168. Which England player holds the record for the most wickets (383)?

169. Who is the player that played the most One Day International matches as captain of England (as of 2007)?

170. Who is the England player that holds the record of the highest individual batting score in One Day Internationals (167 not out)?

ANDREW FLINTOFF

171. In which Lancashire town was Andrew Flintoff born?

172. How did Andrew Flintoff acquire his nickname Freddie
    - A: He was a fan of Freddie Mercury of Queen;
    B: Because his name is similar to that of cartoon
    character Fred Flintstone;
    C: He bowled like Fred Trueman; or
    D: He used to look like members of the band Right
    Said Fred?

173. In what year did Andrew Flintoff make his Test debut
    for England?

174. Against which nation did Andrew Flintoff make his Test
    debut?

175. What is Andrew Flintoff's ODI shirt number?

176. What part of Andrew Flintoff's body has been
    regularly injured due to his bowling action?

177. Which Surrey bowler did Andrew Flintoff once hit for
    34 runs in one over in 1998?

178. In what year did Andrew Flintoff break Ian Botham's
    record of scoring the most sixes for England?

179. Andrew Flintoff was the sixth player to do what on all
    five days of a Test match in Mohali?

180. What is the name of Andrew Flintoff's wife?

RECORDS

181. When Sri Lanka notched up their record innings score of 952/6 in 1997, who were the opponents?

182. Which Australian club holds the world record for the highest innings total in 1926/27 of 1,107?

183. Who equalled Garfield Sobers' record of six sixes in an over playing for Bombay against Baroda in 1984/85?

184. In 1994, which player set a world record of 72 boundaries in an innings?

185. Which player hold the record for the highest career batting average of 95.14?

186. Which bowler holds the record of most wickets in a career (4,204)?

187. Who is considered (based on his career figures) as the best all-rounder of all time?

188. In 1992/93 the West Indies beat Australia by the narrowest winning runs margin. How many runs did they win by?

189. In what season was the most recent (as of 2007) tied Test match played between Australia and India?

190. Which nation scored the least runs in an innings (26) in a match against England in Auckland in 1954/55?

NORTHAMPTONSHIRE

191.   What is Northamptonshire's One Day name?

192.   Which county did Northamptonshire face in its first class debut in 1905?

193.   Who was Northamptonshire's captain in 2007?

194.   How many times had Northamptonshire won the County Cricket Championship as of 2007?

195.   In what year was Northamptonshire CCC founded?

196.   Who was Northamptonshire's coach in 2007?

197.   In what year did Northamptonshire win the Benson and Hedges Cup?

198.   Northamptonshire's highest total was 781 for 7 declared against which county in 1995?

199.   Which Northamptonshire batsman hit 331 not out against Somerset at Taunton in 2003?

200.   In what year did Northamptonshire win the County Championship Division Two?

CRICKET HISTORY

201.   In which century is cricket first mentioned as having
       been played at the Royal Grammer School in
       Guildford?

202.   In what year were the Laws of Cricket first laid down?

203.   How would a bowler deliver the ball to a batsman in
       the early days of cricket - A: Along the ground; B:
       Underarm; C: A throw similar to baseball; or D: Gentle
       over-arm bowl?

204.   In what year was Lords opened? A: 1747; B: 1767;
       C: 1787; or D: 1807?

205.   What period of wars briefly halted the development of
       cricket in the early 1800s?

206.   Which two nations contested the first ever
       international cricket game in 1844 - A: England and
       Scotland; B: England and Australia; C: Canada and the
       USA; or D: Canada and Australia?

207.   In what year did the County Cricket Championship
       begin - A: 1880; B: 1890; C: 1900; or D: 1910?

208.   In what decade did the number of balls per over
       become standardised to 6 - A: 1840s; B: 1880s;
       C: 1920s; or D: 1940s?

209.   In what year did Kerry Packer start World Series cricket
       - A: 1976; B: 1977; C: 1978; or D: 1979?

210.   In what year was Twenty20 Cricket initiated?

GEOFFREY BOYCOTT

211. In what year was Geoff Boycott born?

212. For which South African cricket club did Geoff Boycott play in 1971/72?

213. In what year did Geoff Boycott make his Test debut against Australia?

214. Who was Geoff Boycott's opening partner for England 49 times?

215. How many Test wickets did Geoff Boycott get - A: 3; B: 7; C: 11; or D: 15?

216. In what year did Geoff Boycott play in his last Test match?

217. Which player admitted to deliberately getting Geoff Boycott run out because he was scoring too slowly in a match against Australia in Perth in 1978?

218. Against which nation did Geoff Boycott make his last Test appearance for England?

219. Two of Geoff Boycott's nicknames were Fiery and Thatch, but what was the other?

220. In what year was Geoff Boycott named Wisden Cricketer of the Year?

DARREN GOUGH

221. Where was Darren Gough born?

222. For which County Cricket Club did Darren Gough play between 2004 and 2006?

223. What was Darren Gough's ODI shirt number for Yorkshire in 2007?

224. Against which nation did Darren Gough make his Test debut?

225. In what year did Darren Gough make his Test debut?

226. Darren Gough is known by two nicknames - Rhino and what else?

227. In what year did Darren Gough retire from Test cricket after a knee injury threatened to end his career?

228. Who was Darren Gough's partner when he won the BBC series *Strictly Come Dancing*?

229. In 2006 Darren Gough played in two One Day Internationals for England against which nation?

230. How many Test wickets did Darren Gough get - A: 229; B: 239; C: 249; or D: 259?

WORLD CUP 2007 - 1

231. Name the 16 participants of the 2007 Cricket World Cup.

232. Who was Player of the Tournament for the 2007 Cricket World Cup?

233. What was the name of the Pakistan coach who died under mysterious circumstances during the 2007 Cricket World Cup?

234. Which nation was Australia's first victim in the 2007 Cricket World Cup?

235. What was the only nation that India beat during the 2007 Cricket World Cup?

236. Which two nations did England beat on their way through to the 2007 Cricket World Cup Super 8 stage?

237. Who were the top four nations in the final Super 8 table of the 2007 Cricket World Cup?

238. Which player scored the most runs in the 2007 Cricket World Cup?

239. Which Englishman shared the most catches with Graeme Smith of South Africa?

240. Who was the first player to hit six sixes in a One Day International for South Africa in one over off the bowling of Daan van Bunge of the Netherlands in the 2007 Cricket World Cup?

GRAHAM THORPE

241.   In what year was Graham Thorpe born?

242.   For which County Cricket Club did Graham Thorpe play?

243.   Graham Thorpe retired from Test cricket after which player was selected ahead of him?

244.   In what year did Graham Thorpe make his Test debut against Australia?

245.   In what year was Graham Thorpe awarded the MBE?

246.   Against which nation did Graham Thorpe make his final Test appearance in 2005?

247.   What was Graham Thorpe's nickname?

248.   What is Graham Thorpe's middle name?

249.   In what year did Graham Thorpe make his first class debut?

250.   What was unusual about the century Graham Thorpe scored against Pakistan in November 2000?

SIR DONALD BRADMAN

251.	In what year was Don Bradman born?

252.	What was Don Bradman's nickname?

253.	What was Don Bradman's Test batting average?

254.	Name one of the clubs that Don Bradman played for.

255.	In what Australian town was Don Bradman born?

256.	With which service did Don Bradman serve during the Second World War?

257.	In what year did Don Bradman achieve his 100th first class century?

258.	What career did Don Bradman have after he retired from cricket?

259.	How many Test centuries did Don Bradman hit - A: 29; B: 39; C: 49; or D: 59?

260.	In what year did Don Bradman sadly pass away?

SIR GARFIELD SOBERS

261. On which West Indian island nation was Garfield Sobers born?

262. For which County Cricket Club did Garfield Sobers play between 1968 and 1974?

263. In what year did Garfield Sobers make his Test debut against England?

264. In what year did Garfield Sobers play his last Test match?

265. Against which county was Garfield Sobers playing when he became the first player to hit six sixes in one over in 1968?

266. Garfield Sobers is the author of a children's novel about cricket. What is the title of the book?

267. In what year was Garfield Sobers knighted by the Queen?

268. What was Garfield Sobers' Test batting average
    - A: 51.23; B: 54.43; C: 57.78; or D: 60.91?

269. How many Test wickets did Garfield Sobers get in his career - A: 205; B: 215; C: 225; or D: 235?

270. Against which bowler did Garfield Sobers hit six sixes in a County Cricket match in 1968?

CRICKET ON TV AND IN FILM

271.   In what year was the TV film *Bodyline: It's Just Not Cricket* released in Australia?

272.   In what year was Test cricket first broadcast by the BBC - A: 1938; B: 1947; C: 1953; or D: 1956?

273.   Which actor was associated with wearing a cricket-style costume in his role as Doctor Who?

274.   Who became the first television cricket correspondent for the BBC in 1963?

275.   Who, in the 1970s, innovated such things as the white cricket ball, coloured kits and stump-cams that would subsequently become commonplace in televised cricket?

276.   In what year did Sky TV first acquire the rights to televise County Cricket matches and home One Day Internationals in England?

277.   In what year did the BBC lose its uninterrupted television rights of cricket to Sky TV and Channel Four?

278.   Dennis Compton and Jim Laker appeared in a 1953 film about a man playing the last matches of his career and his poet son disappoints him by not attending his penultimate game. What was the title of the movie?

279.   To mark the conclusion of their 'Third World Week' celebration, a cricket team in a small English village invites a black cricket team from South London to a charity game with comical results. What is the title of this 1987 film, starring Norman Beaton and Robert Urquhart?

280.   In what year did Richie Benaud make his first BBC radio cricket commentary?

SIR VIV RICHARDS

281. What do Viv Richards' initials IVA stand for?

282. What was Viv Richards' nickname, other than Smokey?

283. For which County Cricket Club did Viv Richards play between 1990 and 1993?

284. In what year did Viv Richards make his Test debut for the West Indies against India?

285. How many times did Viv Richards win the cricket World Cup?

286. How many Test wickets did Viv Richards get - A: 12; B: 22; C: 32; or D: 42?

287. In what year did Viv Richards win the Nat West Trophy with Somerset?

288. In what year was Viv Richards named as Wisden Cricketer of the Year?

289. Viv Richards played Association Football for Antigua in a qualifying campaign for what year's FIFA World Cup?

290. With which Bollywood actress does Viv Richards have a daughter?

NEIL FOSTER

291. In what year was Neil born - 1960, 1961 or 1962?

292. How many Test caps did Neil win for England - 25, 27 or 29?

293. Against which country did Neil make his Test debut in 1983?

294. True or false: Neil played 48 ODIs for England?

295. What type of bowler was Neil?

296. In what year was Neil's last Test cap - 1991, 1993 or 1995?

297. Neil's best bowling figures in Test matches were against Pakistan 8/107, in which year?

298. How many runs did Neil score in Test matches - 346, 446 or 546?

299. What was Neil's highest score in a Test?

300. For which county did Neil play - Essex, Leicestershire or Nottinghamshire?

WORLD CUP 2003

301. What nation staged the 2003 Cricket World Cup?

302. England lost all their first Pool A games in the 2003 World Cup against which nation via a walkover?

303. Which nation won Pool B in the 2003 World Cup and was later beaten by Australia in the semi-final?

304. Whom did Australia beat in the 2003 World Cup final?

305. Which Australian player was sent home from the 2003 World Cup after a positive drug test?

306. Which player was voted player of the tournament in the 2003 World Cup?

307. Who was the Sri Lanka bowler that took the most wickets in the 2003 World Cup?

308. Which nation did Canada beat in the 2003 World Cup?

309. Who was the only player to score a century in the 2003 World Cup final?

310. Who was the English umpire in the 2003 World Cup final?

SIR JACK HOBBS

311. For which County Cricket Club did Jack Hobbs play?

312. In what decade did Jack Hobbs make his Test debut?

313. True or false: Jack Hobbs was the youngest of 12 children?

314. How many first class centuries did Jack Hobbs score in his career - A: 9; B: 99; C: 199; or D: 299?

315. What was Jack Hobbs' full name?

316. With which batsman did Jack Hobbs make 11 opening partnerships of 100 runs?

317. Jack Hobbs' 101 not out in the second innings of an August 1926 match against Somerset broke whose record for career centuries?

318. What career did Jack Hobbs take on during the First World War?

319. In what decade was Jack Hobbs knighted?

320. What career did Jack Hobbs take up after he retired from cricket?

SIR IAN BOTHAM

321.   Ian Botham's son Liam played cricket for which County Cricket Club in 1996?

322.   For which Australian club did Ian Botham play?

323.   In what year did Ian Botham make his Test debut?

324.   What is the name of Ian Botham's wife?

325.   For which three County Cricket Clubs did Ian Botham play during his career?

326.   How many times did Ian Botham achieve ten wickets in a Test match - A: 2; B: 4; C: 6; or D: 8?

327.   Ian Botham resigned from his first cricket club in 1985 as a protest against what?

328.   How many ODI centuries did Ian Botham score - A: 0; B: 1; C: 2; or D: 3?

329.   Ian Botham made his last Test appearance in 1992 against which nation?

330.   In what year did Ian Botham first do one of his famous charity walks?

SOUTH AFRICA

331. In what South African city did South Africa play its first Test match against England in 1889?

332. Who was South Africa's captain in 2007?

333. By what other name is the South African cricket team known?

334. Against which nation did South Africa play their first ever One Day International in 1991?

335. Which South African player began his Test career with Australia in the 1980s?

336. Who was South Africa's coach in 2007?

337. In what year did South Africa win the Commonwealth Games gold medal?

338. Which South African captain resigned after failing to get past the group stage of the 2003 World Cup?

339. Against which nation did South Africa achieve a score of 438 for 9 in a 2006 One Day International match?

340. In what year did South Africa win the ICC Knockout Tournament?

DENNIS LILLEE

341. In what decade was Dennis Lillee born?

342. How many Test half-centuries did Dennis Lillee hit in his career - A: 0; B: 1; C: 2; or D: 3?

343. For which club did Dennis Lillee make his first class debut?

344. In what season did Dennis Lillee make his Test debut?

345. With whom did Dennis Lillee form a formidable bowling partnership in 1981?

346. Which Australian wicketkeeper was involved in the most catches off Dennis Lillee's bowling?

347. With which Pakistani batsman did Dennis Lillee have an unsavoury confrontation in 1981, which led to a two match ban?

348. Dennis Lillee made a brief comeback to first class cricket in 1987/88 when he played for which club?

349. How many times did Dennis Lillee achieve a ten-wicket haul in a Test match - A: 3; B: 7; C: 11; or D: 15?

350. In what year did Dennis Lillee play with an aluminium bat?

ASHES HISTORY

Match up the year with the England/Australia score

351.	2005	1-2
352.	2001	1-2
353.	1993	2-1
354.	1985	1-2
355.	1975	1-4
356.	1961	1-0
357.	1953	1-4
358.	1948	3-1
359.	1930	0-1
360.	1909	0-4

WORLD CUP 2007 - 2

361. In the 2007 World Cup the Netherlands chalked up one victory in Group A against which nation?

362. In Group A of the 2007 World Cup, which nation scored the most runs against Australia?

363. India only managed one win in Group B of the 2007 World Cup against which nation?

364. Which player was named Player of the Series in the 2007 World Cup?

365. Which player scored 659 runs, the most in the 2007 WorldCup?

366. Which player scored the first century of the 2007 World Cup?

367. Which nation defeated England by just two runs in Group C of the 2007 World Cup?

368. Which nation defeated Pakistan, knocking them out of the World Cup 2007 at the Group stage?

369. Which player scored the fastest World Cup 100 in 2007, of 60 balls?

370. Which nation did World Cup 2007 runner-up Sri Lanka defeat in the semi-final?

SACHIN TENDULKAR

371. What is Sachin Tendulkar's nickname?

372. What is Sachin Tendulkar's middle name - A: Imran; B: Rahul; C: Sanath; or D: Ramesh?

373. In what year did Sachin Tendulkar make his Test debut against Pakistan?

374. What is Sachin Tendulkar's ODI shirt number?

375. In what city was Sachin Tendulkar born?

376. For which English County Cricket Club did Sachin Tendulkar play in 1992?

377. Who was the match referee that fined Sachin Tendulkar for alleged ball tampering in a Test match against South Africa in 2001?

378. Who was captain of India when Sachin Tendulkar made his debut for India?

379. What event prevented Sachin Tendulkar from playing in a 1999 World Cup match against Zimbabwe?

380. In what year was Sachin Tendulkar born?

WORLD CUP 1999

381. Which Indian player scored the first century of the 1999 World Cup?

382. Which two nations beat Australia in Group B of the 1999 World Cup?

383. Which was the only nation to defeat Pakistan in Group A of the 1999 World Cup?

384. India finished bottom of the Super Six group, only managing a win against one nation - which one?

385. What was unusual about the 1999 World Cup semi-final between Australia and South Africa?

386. Who was Man of the Match in the 1999 World Cup final?

387. Which player was adjudged Player of the Tournament in the 1999 World Cup?

388. Who was the only Pakistan wicket to fall in the 1999 World Cup semi-final against New Zealand?

389. Which Indian player scored the most runs in the 1999 World Cup?

390. Which New Zealand bowler shared the most wickets statistics with Shane Warne in the 1999 World Cup?

WINNERS OF THE HONG KONG SIXES

Match up the year with the winning nation

391.	2005	South Africa
392.	2004	South Indies
393.	2003	Pakistan
394.	2002	England
395.	2001	England
396.	1997	India
397.	1996	England
398.	1995	England
399.	1994	Pakistan
400.	1993	Pakistan

SIR CLYDE WALCOTT

401.　In what decade did Clyde Walcott make his Test debut?

402.　For what nation did Clyde Walcott play?

403.　Clyde Walcott was a member of 'The Three Ws'. Who were the other two?

404.　In later life Clyde Walcott became the first non-English and non-white chairman of what administrative organisation?

405.　True or false: Clyde Walcott admitted that Arsenal footballer Theo Walcott was his nephew?

406.　In what decade did Clyde Walcott play in his last Test match?

407.　What was Clyde Walcott's top Test score - A: 220; B: 260; C: 300; or D: 340?

408.　How many Test wickets did Clyde Walcott take - A: 1; B: 11; C: 21; or D: 31?

409.　In what position did Clyde Walcott field in his first 15 Test matches?

410.　In what year was Clyde Walcott named as Wisden Cricketer of the Year?

CRICKET IN THE USA

411.   Which early American President was believed to be a supporter of cricket?

412.   In which USA city was the first international cricket match held?

413.   The rise of what sport initiated the decline of cricket in the mid-nineteenth century?

414.   In what decade was USA made an Associate Member of the ICC?

415.   In what year did USA win the ICC 6 Nations Challenge Trophy?

416.   What was the name of the USA cricket captain at the end of 2007?

417.   For what reason was the USA suspended as an Associate Member of the ICC in 2007?

418.   Who is generally regarded as the greatest cricketer ever to be produced by the USA - A: Ken Weekes; B: Jehan Mubarak; C: Clayton Lambert; or D: Bart King?

419.   True or false: the USA has never participated in the Cricket World Cup?

420.   Who captained the USA in its first One Day International in 2004?

IMRAN KHAN

421. What is Imran Khan's full name?

422. In what year was Imran Khan born?

423. Where in Pakistan was Imran Khan born?

424. In what year did Imran Khan make his Test debut?

425. Against which nation did Imran Khan play his debut Test and debut ODI?

426. For which County Cricket Club did Imran Khan play between 1971 and 1976?

427. With which club did Imran Khan end his County Cricket days in England in 1988?

428. In what year did Imran Khan play his last Test match?

429. What career did Imran Khan take up on his retirement from cricket?

430. In what year was Imran Khan named as Wisden Cricketer of the Year?

PAKISTAN

431. In what year was Pakistan granted Test status?

432. Against which nation did Pakistan play its first Test match?

433. Who replaced Inzamam-ul-Haq as Pakistan captain after the 2007 World Cup?

434. At what nation's recommendation was Pakistan granted Test status?

435. Who replaced Bob Woolmer and Mushtaq Ahmed as Pakistan coach in 2007?

436. In what year did Pakistan win the Asia Cup?

437. True or false: as of the beginning of 2008, Pakistan has lost more Test matches in its history than it has won?

438. True or false: Pakistan won all three Australasia Cup tournaments between 1986 and 1994?

439. How many times has Pakistan reached at least the semi-finals of the World Cup?

440. Which two Pakistani cities have staged the most Test matches?

MICHAEL VAUGHAN

441. What is Michael Vaughan's middle name - John, Paul, George or Richard?

442. What is Michael Vaughan's nickname?

443. In what year did Michael Vaughan make his County Cricket debut?

444. In what year did Michael Vaughan make his Test debut?

445. Against which nation did Michael Vaughan make his Test debut?

446. In what year was Michael Vaughan made England captain?

447. In what year did Michael Vaughan take 4/46 and score 92 versus Leicestershire in the B&H at Leicester?

448. How many Test wickets had Michael Vaughan taken by the end of 2007 - A: 5; B: 6; C: 7; or D: 8?

449. In 2004 Michael Vaughan scored 140 in the final Test against which nation?

450. In what English city was Michael Vaughan born?

WORLD CUP 1987

451.   Which Australian captain lifted the 1987 World Cup?

452.   Where was the 1987 World Cup staged?

453.   Which batsman scored the most runs in the 1987 World Cup?

454.   Which bowler took the most wickets in the 1987 World Cup?

455.   England qualified from Group B of the 1987 World Cup in second place, but who won the group?

456.   Who scored a century in the opening match of the 1987 World Cup for Pakistan against Sri Lanka?

457.   Who scored a century for England in the 1987 World Cup semi-final victory against India?

458.   Which Australian was the top scorer in the 1987 World Cup final scoring 75 runs against England?

459.   Name one of the umpires for the 1987 World Cup final?

460.   Which company sponsored the 1987 World Cup?

JIM LAKER

461. In what decade was Jim Laker born?

462. Which two County Cricket Clubs did Jim Laker play for?

463. In what year was Jim Laker named as Wisden cricketer of the year?

464. Against which nation did Jim Laker make his Test debut?

465. In what year did Jim Laker win the BBC Sports Personality of the Year award?

466. At which ground did Jim Laker take 19 wickets in a Test match against Australia in 1956?

467. In what year did Jim Laker play in his last Test match against Australia at Melbourne?

468. Jim Laker's record breaking 19 wickets in a Test match against Australia in 1956 was at the expense of how many runs - A: 60; B: 70; C: 80; or D: 90?

469. What career did Jim Laker take up in later life?

470. In what year did Jim Laker sadly pass away?

COUNTY CRICKET - 1

471. Which eight counties competed in the very first County Cricket Championship in 1890?

472. Which of the current County Cricket Clubs joined in 1992?

473. Which club won the County Cricket Division Two Championship in 2007?

474. In what year was the County Cricket Championship split into two divisions?

475. Which club won the first three County Cricket Championships (1880 to 1882)?

476. Which club won the County Cricket Championship both in 1901 and in 2001?

477. Which four clubs had never won a County Cricket Championship as of 2007?

478. Which club has won the most County Cricket Championships?

479. Which club has won the most Wooden Spoons (finished bottom of the league) in the County Cricket Championship?

480. Which company was the first to sponsor the County Cricket Championship in 1977?

CURTLY AMBROSE

481.   In what year was Curtly Ambrose born?

482.   What is Curtly Ambrose's nickname?

483.   Curtly Ambrose was born on which West Indian island?

484.   In what year did Curtly Ambrose make his Test debut?

485.   For which County Cricket Club did Curtly Ambrose play between 1989 and 1996?

486.   Against which nation did Curtly Ambrose make his ODI debut?

487.   How many Test wickets did Curtly Ambrose take in his career - A: 385; B: 395; C: 405; or D: 415?

488.   True or false: Curtly Ambrose hit one Test half-century in his career?

489.   In what year did Curtly Ambrose play in his last Test match?

490.   Curtly Ambrose plays in a band called Big Band Dread with which former West Indies teammate?

MIKE BREARLEY

491. Mike Brearley is known by his middle name, but what is his first name?

492. How many Test wickets did Mike Brearley take - A: 0; B: 1; C: 2; or D: 3?

493. In what year did Mike Brearley make his Test debut?

494. Against which nation did Mike Brearley make his Test debut?

495. Mike Brearley made his County Cricket debut with which club?

496. In 2007 Mike Brearley was President Designate of which cricket club?

497. Where was Mike Brearley born?

498. In what decade was Mike Brearley born?

499. Who captained England in between Mike Brearley's two spells as captain?

500. With what honour was Mike Brearley presented by Her Majesty the Queen in 1978?

MORE ON BEEFY

501.   In what year did Ian Botham win the BBC Sports Personality of the Year award?

502.   In what year was Ian Botham named as Wisden Cricketer of the Year?

503.   For what reason was Ian Botham briefly banned in 1986?

504.   Which football club offered Ian Botham a place as a teenager?

505.   In what position did Ian Botham play while at Scunthorpe United FC?

506.   In what year did Ian Botham make the first of his 11 League appearances for Scunthorpe United?

507.   In addition to Scunthorpe, for which other football club did Ian Botham play?

508.   From and to which places did Ian Botham do his first charity walk?

509.   In what year was Ian Botham knighted by Her Majesty the Queen?

510.   Ian Botham was the first president of which charity?

SOMERSET

511. How many times has Somerset won the County Championship Wooden Spoon (finished bottom of the league)?

512. In what year was Somerset County Cricket Club founded?

513. Which bowler holds the record for the most wickets for Somerset (2,165)?

514. Which batsman holds the record for scoring the most runs for Somerset (21,142)?

515. What is Somerset's name in One Day cricket?

516. Where is Somerset's cricketing headquarters?

517. In what year did Somerset win the first of its three Gillette/NatWest/C&G trophies?

518. Against which county did Somerset achieve a score of 850 for 7 declared in 2007?

519. Which Australian player scored Somerset's highest individual batting total (342) against Surrey in 2006?

520. In what year did Somerset win the Twenty20 Cup?

WORLD CUP 1992

521. In which nation was the 1992 Cricket World Cup staged?

522. Who was named as Player of the Series in the 1992 World Cup?

523. Which nation won the group stage of the 1992 World Cup?

524. Which bowler took the most wickets in the 1992 World Cup (18)?

525. Which English bowler took 16 wickets during the 1992 World Cup?

526. Which nation did England knock out of the World Cup semi-final?

527. Zimbabwe scored 312 for 4 but still lost its first World Cup match to which nation?

528. Which Australian scored a century in his first and last game of the 1992 World Cup?

529. Which Pakistan player scored the most runs as his side went on to beat England in the 1992 World Cup final?

530. Which was the only nation to be beaten by Zimbabwe during the 1992 World Cup?

DURHAM

531. In what year was Durham County Cricket Club founded?

532. Which South African captained Durham in 2007?

533. What is the capacity of the Riverside Ground?

534. Which club did Durham first entertain at the Riverside Ground on 18 May 1995?

535. What, in simple terms, is the design on the Durham CCC shield?

536. Who was the Durham coach that led the club to its first major title in 2007?

537. Who was the first side to visit Durham's Riverside Ground to play England in a 2003 Test match?

538. What competition did Durham win on beating Hampshire at Lords in August 2007?

539. What legendary Australian batsman led Durham between 1997 and 1999?

540. What is Durham's One Day name?

WALLY HAMMOND

541. In what decade was Wally Hammond born?

542. For which County Cricket Club did Wally Hammond play?

543. Where was Wally Hammond born?

544. In what year did Wally Hammond make his Test debut - A: 1925; B: 1926; C: 1927; or D: 1928?

545. In what fielding position was Wally Hammond regarded as one of the best the game of cricket has ever seen?

546. True or false: Wally Hammond's top score was 236 not out against New Zealand in Aukland?

547. Why did Wally Hammond revert from a professional to an amateur in 1938?

548. In what year did Wally Hammond play his last Test match - A: 1946; B: 1947; C: 1948; or D: 1949?

549. How many Test wickets did Wally Hammond take - A: 83; B: 93; C: 103; or D: 113?

550. In what decade did Wally Hammond sadly pass away?

YOUNG CRICKETER OF THE YEAR

Match up the year with the player who won the title

551.	1979	**Andrew Flintoff**
552.	1969	**Owais Shah**
553.	1957	**Paul Parker**
554.	1996	**Alastair Cook**
555.	2001	**Neil Foster**
556.	2005	**Micky Stewart**
557.	1998	**Mike Gatting**
558.	1983	**Alan Ward**
559.	1990	**Chris Silverwood**
560.	1981	**Michael Atherton**

SRI LANKA

561. By what name was the nation of Sri Lanka known before 1972?

562. In 2007 Sri Lanka scored 260 for 6 in a Twenty20 match against which nation?

563. Who is Sri Lanka's record wicket taker in Test matches and One Day Internationals as of 2007?

564. Which Sri Lankan batsman has scored the highest aggregate of runs in Test cricket?

565. Which Sri Lankan has played the most Test matches as captain as of 2007?

566. Against which nation did Sri Lanka play its first ever Test match?

567. Who was the Sri Lankan captain in 2007?

568. Who was the Australian Sri Lankan coach in 2007?

569. In what year did Sri Lanka beat England 5-0 in a Test series in England?

570. Which Sri Lankan batsman has scored the most Test centuries for his nation as of 2007?

RICHIE BENAUD

571.   In what decade was Richie Benaud born?

572.   In which Australian state was Richie Benaud born?

573.   In what year did Richie Benaud make his Test debut?

574.   Against which nation did Richie Benaud make his Test debut?

575.   Against which nation did Richie Benaud make his highest Test score in 1957/58?

576.   True or false: in 1963 Richie Benaud became the first Test player to complete the double of 200 wickets and 2,000 runs?

577.   In what year did Richie Benaud play in his last Test match?

578.   With what phrase did Richie Benaud always greet viewers to cricket at the beginning of a televised match?

579.   What was the name of Richie Benaud's younger brother who also played cricket for Australia?

580.   What was the title of Richie Benaud's book published in 2005?

MIKE GATTING

581. In what year was Mike Gatting born?

582. Mike Gatting's brother Steve and son Joe have played for which Football League club?

583. What is Mike Gatting's middle name?

584. For what County Cricket Club did Mike Gatting play?

585. In what year did Mike Gatting make his Test debut?

586. Against which nation did Mike Gatting make his Test debut?

587. Which player replaced Mike Gatting as England captain?

588. What was Mike Gatting's top Test score - A: 197; B: 207; C: 217; or D: 227?

589. In what year did Mike Gatting play his last Test match against Australia?

590. In what year did Mike Gatting retire from first class cricket?

SUNIL GAVASKAR

591.   In what decade was Sunil Gavaskar born?

592.   Which player broke Sunil Gavaskar's record of 34 Test centuries in 2005?

593.   In what year did Sunil Gavaskar make his Test debut?

594.   What is Sunil Gavaskar's top Test score - A: 236; B: 246; C: 256; or D: 266?

595.   What is Sunil Gavaskar's nickname?

596.   How many Test wickets did Sunil Gavaskar take in his career - A: 0; B: 1; C: 2; or D: 3?

597.   Against which nation did Sunil Gavaskar make his Test debut?

598.   Who replaced Sunil Gavaskar as captain of India in 1985?

599.   Against which nation did Sunil Gavaskar make his last Test appearance, scoring 96 runs in his second innings of the match?

600.   What is the name of Sunil Gavaskar's ODI international son?

THE LORDS TAVERNERS

601. In what decade was the Lords Taverners first formed?

602. Which actor was the first President of the Lords Taverners?

603. In what year did the Lords Taverners play its first match against Bishops Stortford CC?

604. The Lords Taverners claims to be the pioneer of what current day cricket format?

605. Which member of the royal family became President of the Lords Taverners in 1960?

606. For what cause does the Lords Taverners raise half of its charity earnings?

607. Which lyricist was President of the Lords Taverners from 1988 to 1990 and again in 2000?

608. What is the name of the non-celebrity and non-fund-raising team of the Lords Taverners?

609. To within 50 above or below and rounded down to the nearest 100, how many minibuses has the Lords Taverners provided for various charities from 1975 until 2007?

610. Which *Daily Mirror* cartoonist took over from Mike Gatting as President of the Lords Taverners in 2007?

BASIL D'OLIVEIRA

611.   In what decade was Basil D'Oliveira born?

612.   Where was Basil D'Oliveira born?

613.   For which County Cricket Club did Basil D'Oliveira play?

614.   In what year did Basil D'Oliveira make his Test debut for England?

615.   Basil D'Oliveira's nicknames were Baz and what else?

616.   What is the name of Basil D'Oliveira's brother who played for Leicestershire?

617.   Who was the broadcaster responsible for persuading Basil D'Oliveira to emigrate to England?

618.   In what year was Basil D'Oliveira awarded the OBE?

619.   In what year did Basil D'Oliveira play in his last Test match against Australia?

620.   In what year did Basil D'Oliveira retire from first class cricket?

MCC

621. What do the initials MCC stand for?

622. In what year was the MCC founded - A: 1787; B: 1797; C: 1807; or D: 1817?

623. What was the name of the founder of the MCC - A: Lord Taverner; B: Lord Marylebone; C: Thomas Lord; or D: George Lord?

624. What are the colours of the MCC?

625. Until 1998 only one woman (other than domestic staff) was permitted to enter the MCC Pavilion club. Who was she?

626. The MCC evolved from which previous club?

627. Where was the Lords Cricket Ground originally sited?

628. On what road is Lords Cricket Ground currently sited?

629. In what year did the current Lords Cricket Ground open?

630. What is the end opposite the Pavilion End at Lords Cricket Ground called?

WORLD CUP 1996

631.   Who sponsored the 1996 World Cup?

632.   Which countries hosted the 1996 World Cup?

633.   Who was named as Player of the Series of the 1996 World Cup?

634.   Who took the most wickets during the 1996 World Cup?

635.   Who scored the most runs during the 1996 World Cup?

636.   Name one of the two nations that England beat in Group B of the 1996 World Cup?

637.   Which New Zealander scored the first century of the 1996 World Cup (101against England)?

638.   What was special about the way Sri Lanka won the 1996 World Cup semi-final against India?

639.   Who scored a century in the final of the 1996 World Cup?

640.   Which nation was on the losing side in the 1996 World Cup final against Sri Lanka?

HAT-TRICKS

641. Australia's Jimmy Matthews is the only bowler to get two hat-tricks in the same Test match - on 28 May 1912 against which nation?

642. Who has taken two Test and two One Day International hat-tricks in his career?

643. Who was the Australian bowler that took a hat-trick on his Test debut against Pakistan in 1994?

644. Who is the only bowler ever to take four wickets in four balls in international cricket?

645. When Australian bowler Shane Warne took a hat-trick against England in December 1994, who was the third English wicket to fall?

646. Who was the English bowler that got a hat-trick against Australia in January 1999 in Sydney?

647. When Dominic Cork got his hat-trick for England at Old Trafford in 1995, which nation was it against?

648. Which West Indian fast bowler got a hat-trick against Australia in 1988 at Brisbane Cricket Ground?

649. Which English bowler got a hat-trick against the West Indies at the Kensington Oval, Barbados, in 2004?

650. Who took England's first One Day International hat-trick against Pakistan at The Oval on 20 June 2003?

BODYLINE

651. In what season was the Bodyline series played - A: 1930/31; B: 1931/32; C: 1932/33; or D: 1933/34?

652. What bowling theory was Bodyline based on?

653. Who was England's captain during the Bodyline series?

654. Who were the three England fast bowlers employed to carry out the Bodyline tactics?

655. Who was Australia's captain for the Bodyline series?

656. By which margin did England regain the Ashes from Australia in 1932/33?

657. Who was the Australian batsman that suffered a fractured skull after a non-Bodyline delivery deflected from his bat?

658. Which nation adopted Bodyline tactics when they toured England in 1933?

659. In what year were the laws of cricket changed so that Bodyline tactics became illegal?

660. Who was the Australian journalist who coined the term Bodyline - A: Jack Worrall; B: Jack Fingleton; C: Hugh Buggy; or D: Joseph Lyons?

ONE DAY INTERNATIONALS - 2

661. As of 2007, who has umpired in the most One Day Internationals?

662. Who is the Indian player that has taken over 330 One Day International catches?

663. Who is the most prolific wicketkeeper in One Day International history?

664. England's highest team score in One Day International history was 391 for 4 after 50 overs against which nation in 2005?

665. Who is the most economic bowler in One Day International history, of those who have bowled at least 1,500 balls, with a bowling average of just 18.84?

666. Who is the most prolific English wicket taker in One Day International history?

667. One Sri Lankan and one Indian player have made over 800 One Day International appearances between them. Name them.

668. Which Englishman was named ICC One Day International Player of the Year in 2004?

669. Who won the ICC One Day International Player of the Year in 2007?

670. Which player, with a Test batting average of over 50 runs, only played in one One Day International match in which he failed to score?

NOTTINGHAMSHIRE

671. By what One Day name is Nottinghamshire County Cricket Club known?

672. In what year was Nottinghamshire County Cricket Club formed - A: 1841; B: 1851; C: 1861; or D: 1871?

673. How many times had Nottinghamshire won the County Cricket Championship by 2007?

674. In what year did Nottinghamshire win the Benson and Hedges Cup?

675. Who was captain of Nottinghamshire in 2007?

676. Which player scored 31,592 runs for Nottinghamshire in his career?

677. Which player took 1,653 wickets for Nottinghamshire in his career?

678. Nottinghamshire's top score was 791 in 2007 against which county?

679. Who was the New Zealand player that played for Nottinghamshire between 1978 and 1987?

680. Which legendary Bodyline bowler played for Nottinghamshire?

THE WEST INDIES

681.   By what other name is the West Indies cricket team known?

682.   Against which nation did Carl Hooper make his Test debut in 1987-88?

683.   What scene is depicted in the West Indies badge?

684.   Who was the Australian coach of the West Indies cricket team in 2007?

685.   In 2003/04 the West Indies achieved a Test innings total of 751 for 5 declared against which nation?

686.   Who, as of 2007, is the only West Indies bowler to have got a hat-trick when he achieved the feat in an ICC Champions Trophy match against Australia in 2006?

687.   Who was the West Indies captain in 2007?

688.   Which West Indies cricket stadium has staged the most Test matches - A: Sabina Park, Kingston; B: Kensington Oval, Bridgetown; C: Bourda, Guyana; or D: Queen's Park Oval, Port of Spain, Trinidad?

689.   Who was the West Indies team manager in 2007?

690.   In what year did the West Indies win the ICC Champions Trophy?

SIR RICHARD HADLEE

691. In what year was Richard Hadlee born?

692. What was Richard Hadlee's nickname?

693. Against which nation did Richard Hadlee make his Test and ODI debut in 1973?

694. In what year did Richard Hadlee play his last Test match against England?

695. What was Richard Hadlee's bowling style?

696. For which New Zealand club did Richard Hadlee play between 1971 and 1989?

697. What was Richard Hadlee's top batting score in Test matches - A: 141 not out; B: 151 not out; C: 161 not out; or D: 171 not out?

698. In what year was Richard Hadlee knighted?

699. What event did Richard Hadlee state as being his most embarrassing moment in cricket - A: Being bowled out by a part-time bowler; B: Being struck in the box as a batsman off a slow delivery; C: Tripping up on a run-up to bowl; or D: Dropping a really easy catch that would have won a match that his team went on to lose.

700. What is Richard Hadlee's most prized possession - A: The medal he received from the Queen when he was knighted; B: An autograph book containing thousands of cricketers' signatures; C: A bat once used by W.G. Grace; or D: The ball he used when he got a hat-trick?

MIDDLESEX

701. At what ground does Middlesex play most of its home games?

702. What is Middlesex's One Day name?

703. In what year was Middlesex formed?

704. Who was the captain of Middlesex in 2007?

705. What crest do Middlesex players wear on their jerseys?

706. Who is the player that has taken the most wickets for Middlesex?

707. Which Arsenal Football League Champion also won the County Championship with Middlesex in 1950?

708. As of 2007, how many times has Middlesex won the County Championship including shared titles?

709. In what year did Middlesex first win the Benson and Hedges Cup?

710. Who was the Middlesex coach in 2007?

WORLD CUP 1983

711. Which batsman scored the most runs in the 1983 Cricket World Cup?

712. Who scored a century for England in the opening game of the 1983 World Cup against New Zealand?

713. Which nation beat the West Indies by 34 runs in Group B of the 1983 World Cup?

714. Which Indian bowler took the most wickets at the 1983 World Cup?

715. Zimbabwe gained a surprise 13 run victory against which nation at the 1983 World Cup?

716. How did the trophy won by India at the 1983 World Cup get damaged?

717. India's Kapil Dev scored 175 not out in a Group B match against Zimbabwe but the innings was never recorded on video. Why?

718. Which nation did the West Indies defeat in the 1983 World Cup semi-final?

719. How many matches were played in total in the 1983 World Cup?

720. Dickie Bird was one of the umpires in the 1983 World Cup final but who was the other?

SUSSEX

721. In what year was Sussex County Cricket Club founded?

722. What is Sussex's One Day name?

723. Who was the Sussex captain in 2007?

724. At which ground does Sussex play most of its home games?

725. In what year did Sussex win its first official County Championship?

726. After Sussex won the 2007 County Championship, how many times had they won it in total?

727. In what year did Sussex win the Division Two County Championship?

728. 335 not out against Leicestershire in 2003 was achieved by which Sussex batsman?

729. What mythological bird is featured on the Sussex crest?

730. Can you name the batsman who scored 34,150 runs for Sussex during his career?

CRICKETING TERMS - 1

Supply the cricketing term for each of the following descriptions

731. A left-handed bowler bowling wrist spin (left arm unorthodox).

732. A lower-order batsman sent in when the light is dimming to play out the remaining overs of the day in order to protect more valuable batsmen for the next day's play.

733. The half of the pitch in front of the batsman's body as he takes strike.

734. The batsman hits the ball with his bat but only succeeds in diverting it onto the stumps.

735. A dismissal by LBW: indisputable, obvious.

736. Verbal abuse in simple terms, or a psychological tactic in more complex terms. Used by cricketers both on and off the field to gain advantage over the opposition by frustrating them and breaking their concentration.

737. A (usually fast) delivery that is pitched very close to the batsman.

738. A dismissal (for zero) off the first ball of a team's innings.

739. A ball that fails to bounce as high as expected after hitting the pitch.

740. A mathematically based rule that derives a target score for the side batting second in a rain-affected One Day match.

WORLD TWENTY20 2007

741. Which nation hosted the 2007 World Twenty20?

742. Who was named as Player of the Series in the 2007 World Twenty20?

743. Who scored the most runs in the 2007 World Twenty20?

744. Who took the most wickets in the 2007 World Twenty20?

745. Who scored 117 for the West Indies in its opening match against South Africa in the 2007 World Twenty20?

746. Which was the only side that England managed to beat during the 2007 World Twenty20?

747. Who were the two losing semi-finalists in the 2007 World Twenty20?

748. Who was the English umpire in the 2007 World Twenty20 final?

749. Which batsman scored the most runs in the 2007 World Twenty20 final?

750. Yuvraj Singh (India) hit the longest six of the tournament (119m). Who was the Australian bowler?

LADIES CRICKET

751.   Who led England's first ladies Test cricket tour to Australia in 1934/35?

752.   Who was England ladies cricket captain in 2007?

753.   How many times has England won the Ladies World Cup?

754.   England ladies' best One Day International score was 376 for 2 in 1997 against which nation?

755.   Who set a world record when she scored 179 against Australia at the Oval in 1976?

756.   Who was the best known ladies cricketer in the 1930s?

757.   In 1951, which English lady bowler got five wickets in a first innings against Australia?

758.   To date the England ladies cricket team has appeared in all seven European Championship finals. Which nation won the tournament in 2001?

759.   According to the *Reading Mercury*, in what year was the first women's cricket match played - A: 1695; B: 1745; C: 1825; or D: 1915?

760.   What was the name of the first women's cricket club?

DAVID GOWER

761. In what year was David Gower born?

762. Where was David Gower born?

763. Name one of David Gower's three nicknames.

764. For which two County Cricket Clubs did David Gower play?

765. Against which nation did David Gower make his Test debut in 1978?

766. How many Test wickets did David Gower take - A: 0; B: 1; C: 2; or D: 3?

767. Who did David Gower replace when he first became England captain in 1983/84?

768. True or false: David Gower played in a record 119 consecutive Test matches without scoring a duck?

769. In what year did David Gower play in his last Test match?

770. On what BBC comedy panel quiz show was David Gower a captain?

SURREY

771.   In what year was Surrey County Cricket Club formed?

772.   What is Surrey's One Day name?

773.   Who was the Surrey captain in 2007?

774.   What is Surrey's home ground?

775.   What are Surrey's club colours?

776.   What is Surrey's club crest?

777.   In what year did Surrey first win the Twenty20 Cup?

778.   In 1950 Surrey shared the County Championship with which county?

779.   Surrey made a One Day world record in 2007, scoring 496 for 4 in 50 overs against whom?

780.   Who scored 301 not out for Surrey against Northamptonshire in 2006?

WORLD CUP 1979

781. Which company sponsored the 1979 World Cup?

782. In which country was the 1979 World Cup held?

783. Which nation is missing from this list of participants in the 1979 World Cup - Australia, England, India, New Zealand, Pakistan, the West Indies, Sri Lanka?

784. Which West Indies batsman scored the most runs in the 1979 World Cup?

785. Which English bowler took the most wickets in the 1979 World Cup?

786. Who was the captain of the winning West Indies team?

787. Which nation only required 46 for 2 to win one of its matches in the 1979 World Cup?

788. Who was captain of Australia in the 1979 World Cup?

789. Which player scored 138 not out in the 1979 World Cup final?

790. Which nation did England defeat in the 1979 World Cup semi-final?

MALCOLM MARSHALL

791.   In what decade was Malcolm Marshall born?

792.   For which County Cricket Club did Malcolm Marshall play?

793.   What was Malcolm Marshall's top Test score as a batsman - A: 72; B: 82; C: 92; or D: 102?

794.   What is Malcolm Marshall's middle name?

795.   Against which nation did Malcolm Marshall make his 1978 Test debut?

796.   In what year did Malcolm Marshall make his ODI debut?

797.   In what year did Malcolm Marshall play in his last ODI match for the West Indies?

798.   How many Test wickets did Malcolm Marshall take in his career - A: 356; B: 366; C: 376; or D: 386?

799.   In what year did Malcolm Marshall sadly pass away after a battle with cancer?

800.   Malcolm Marshall was born and died in the same Barbados city. Which one?

FRED TRUEMAN

801. What was Fred Trueman's middle name - A: Leawards; B: Maywards; C: Sewards; or D: Kelwards?

802. In what decade was Fred Trueman born?

803. In 1972 Fred Trueman appeared in six One Day matches for which County Cricket Club?

804. What was the name of the 1970s Yorkshire TV series that was presented by Fred Trueman?

805. On which BBC sitcom did Fred Trueman once make a guest appearance?

806. Fred Trueman appeared as a cricket commentator on which BBC radio series written by Douglas Adams?

807. In what year did Fred Trueman make his Test debut?

808. In what year did Fred Trueman play in his last Test match?

809. Fred Trueman's daughter Rebecca married the son of which Hollywood star?

810. In what year did Fred Trueman sadly pass away?

KENT

811.   What is the name of Kent's home ground?

812.   What is Kent's One Day name?

813.   In what year was Kent Cricket Club founded?

814.   In what year did Kent first win the Twenty20 Cup?

815.   In what year did Kent first win the County Championship?

816.   Who was Kent captain in 2007?

817.   In 1977 Kent shared the County Cricket Championship with which other club?

818.   Which player has scored the most runs in Kent's history?

819.   Which bowler took 1951 wicket during his Kent career?

820.   In what year did Kent first win the Benson and Hedges Cup?

BRIAN JOHNSTONE

821. What is true of Brian Johnstone's grandfather - A: He was a Member of Parliament; B: He played first class cricket for Surrey; C: He was a Governor of the Bank of England; or D: He was convicted of murder and hung for his crime?

822. True of false: Brian Johnstone played County Cricket before the Second World War?

823. What was Brian Johnstone's nickname?

824. What medal was Brian Johnstone awarded for his services in the Second World War in 1945?

825. Who was England playing when Brian Johnstone commentated of his first Test match in 1946?

826. Which one of the following TV shows did Brian Johnstone present - A: *What's my line?*; B: *Match of the Day*; C: *Panorama*; or D: *Come Dancing*?

827. What was Brian Johnstone's alleged commentary gaffe when Michael Holding of the West Indies was bowling to England's Peter Willey in a Test match at the Oval in 1976?

828. What was the name of the cricket radio programme that Brian Johnstone was a regular on right up to his death?

829. What nickname did Brian Johnstone create for fellow commentator Bill Frindall?

830. In what year did Brian Johnstone sadly pass away?

CLIVE LLOYD

831. In what year was Clive Lloyd born?

832. In what South American nation was Clive Lloyd born?

833. Name one of Clive Lloyd's two nicknames.

834. What is the name of Clive Lloyd's cousin who also played for the West Indies?

835. In what year did Clive Lloyd make his Test debut against India?

836. How many Test wickets did Clive Lloyd take in his career - A: 7; B: 8; C: 9; or D: 10?

837. In what year did Clive Lloyd first feature as a Test match referee?

838. In what year did Clive Lloyd play in his last Test match against Australia in Sydney?

839. In what year was Clive Lloyd named as Wisden Cricketer of the Year?

840. For which County Cricket club did Clive Lloyd play?

CRICKETING TERMS - 2

Supply the cricketing term for each of the following descriptions

841. A deceptive spinning delivery by a leg spin bowler, also known (particularly in Australia) as the wrong 'un.

842. A close fielder near the slip fielders.

843. A delivery that is much too short to be a good length delivery, but without the sharp lift of a bouncer. Usually considered a bad delivery to bowl as the bats man has a lot of time to see the ball and play an attacking shot.

844. An over in which no runs are scored off the bat, and no wides or no balls are bowled.

845. Two wickets taken off two consecutive deliveries.

846. A bouncer on or just outside off-stump that passes within inches of the batsman's face (so called as the ball is supposedly so close that the batsman can smell it).

847. A pitch on which spin bowlers can turn the ball prodigiously.

848. A hard shot, usually in the air, across the line of a full-pitched ball, aiming to hit the ball over the boundary at cow corner, with very little regard to proper technique.

849. A relatively new off spin delivery developed by Saqlain Mushtaq.

850. A wicket that is considered to be good for batting on, offering little, if any, help for a bowler.

WORLD CUP 1975

851.   Which eight nations competed in the 1975 World Cup?

852.   Which nation only managed a score of 93 all out in the World Cup semi-final?

853.   Which batsman scored the most runs in the 1975 World Cup, 333 in total?

854.   Which bowler took the most wickets in the 1975 World Cup, 11 in total?

855.   Which batsman scored a century for England in the opening match of the 1975 World Cup against India?

856.   Which batsman scored a century in the 1975 World Cup final for the West Indies?

857.   Five Australian players were run out in the 1975 World Cup final, three of them by one West Indies player. Name him.

858.   Which ground staged the 1975 World Cup semi-final between England and Australia?

859.   Dickie Bird and which other umpire officiated at the 1975 World Cup final?

860.   Who was the England captain during the 1975 World Cup?

NEW ZEALAND

861. By what other name is the New Zealand cricket team also known?

862. In relation to the previous question, what year did New Zealand first use its new name?

863. Which nation did New Zealand dismiss twice in one day in 2005?

864. In 2007 New Zealand was the victim of the largest cricket World Cup losing margin (215 runs) against which nation?

865. Which father/son New Zealand bowlers took over 100 Test wickets each during their careers?

866. Which batsman set a record for the highest One Day cricket innings by a New Zealander against Zimbabwe in Harare in 2005?

867. Which New Zealand batsman scored the fastest ever Test double century against England in Christchurch in 2002?

868. Which New Zealander set a record for the longest time taken to score a duck (77 balls in 101 minutes for zero runs) in 1999 against South Africa?

869. Which New Zealander held the record for the most ducks in Test Cricket until he was overtaken by Courtney Walsh of the West Indies?

870. Brian Hastings and which other batsman together scored 151 runs for the highest ever 10th-wicket partnership against Pakistan in 1973?

BISHAN BEDI

871. In what decade was Bishan Bedi born?

872. In what Indian state was Bishan Bedi born?

873. For which County Cricket Club did Bishan Bedi play?

874. In what year did Bishan Bedi make his Test debut?

875. Who was Bishan Bedi's first Test wicket - A: Basil Butcher; B: Clive Lloyd; C: Garry Sobers; or D: Lance Gibbs?

876. In what year did Bishan Bedi make his ODI debut against England at Headingley?

877. What was Bishan Bedi's top Test score - A: 40; B: 50; C: 60; or D: 70?

878. How many Test wickets did Bishan Bedi take in his career - A: 233; B: 244; C: 255; or D: 266?

879. In what year did Bishan Bedi play in his last Test match?

880. Of which Sri Lankan bowler has Bishan Bedi been a vehement critic because of his bowling action?

WARWICKSHIRE

881.   In what year was Warwickshire County Cricket Club founded?

882.   What is Warwickshire's One Day name?

883.   Who has scored the most first class runs for Warwickshire?

884.   As of 2007, how many times had Warwickshire won the County Cricket Championship?

885.   Against which county did Warwickshire gain its highest team total (810 for 4 declared) in 1994?

886.   Which batsman set the highest individual score for Warwickshire (501 not out) in 1994?

887.   Which Warwickshire bowler set the best bowling figures record for the club with 10 wickets for 41 runs against the Combined Services in 1959?

888.   Warwickshire bowled which county out for 15 on one occasion and still lost the match by 155 runs?

889.   True or false: father and son combination William and Bernard Quaife batted alongside each other for Warwickshire in 1922?

890.   Who was Warwickshire's coach in 2007?

MIKE PROCTER

891. In what decade was Mike Procter born?

892. What was Mike Procter's nickname?

893. Where was Mike Procter born?

894. For which County Cricket Club did Mike Procter play?

895. In what year did Mike Procter make his Test debut?

896. Mike Procter made his last Test appearance in 1970 against which nation?

897. In what year was Mike Procter named Wisden Cricketer of the Year?

898. As Director of Coaching, which County Cricket Club did Mike Procter lead to the Nat West Trophy in 1989/90?

899. In what year was Mike Procter first a Test match referee?

900. Mike Procter's father, brother and cousin all played first class cricket. Name one of them (first name).

STEVE WAUGH

901. *In what year was Steve Waugh born?*

902. *What was Steve Waugh's nickname?*

903. *For which English county did Steve Waugh play in 2002?*

904. *In what year did Steve Waugh make his Test debut for Australia?*

905. *For which Australian club did Steve Waugh play?*

906. *In what year was Steve Waugh named Australian of the Year?*

907. *In what year did Steve Waugh play his last Test match?*

908. *What was Steve Waugh's bowling style?*

909. *How many times did Steve Waugh get five wickets in Test innings - A: 1; B: 2; C: 3; or D: 4?*

910. *How many Test runs did Steve Waugh get in his career - A: 9,927; B: 10,927; C: 11,927; or D: 12,927?*

COUNTY CRICKET - 2

911. Which Gloucestershire all-rounder bowled a hat-trick and scored a century in the same match twice, once against Essex in 1972 and then against Leicestershire in 1979?

912. In 1974, which county was unbeaten in the County Championship but only finished in eighth position in the table?

913. In 1982, which county went through the whole season without winning one County Championship match?

914. In 1967, which county drew 24 of its 28 County Championship matches?

915. How old was the oldest player ever to have played in a County Championship - A: 47; B: 57; C: 67; or D: 77?

916. The highest number of consecutive appearances in the County Championship is 423 by Ken Suttle for which county?

917. In 1969, which county won the County Championship with an unbeaten record?

918. Which county holds the record for the highest number of victories during a County Championship season (25 in 1923)?

919. Which county struggled for four years (1935 to 1939) without winning a County Championship match?

920. Which county held the record for the most defeats in a season (20) when they set it with a poor 1925 season?

WASIM AKRAM

921. In what year was Wasim Akram born?

922. What is Wasim Akram's nickname?

923. What County Cricket Club did Wasim Akram sign for in 1988?

924. What County Cricket Club did Wasim Akram join before his retirement in 2003?

925. In what year did Wasim Akram make his Test debut against New Zealand?

926. Who once said the following of Wasim Akram: "Over my 15 or 16 years of playing international cricket in Tests and One Day Internationals, Wasim Akram is definitely the most outstanding bowler I've ever faced"?

927. In what year did Wasim Akram play in his last Test match?

928. How many wickets did Wasim Akram take in ODIs - A: 202; B: 302; C: 402; or D: 502?

929. What was Wasim Akram's biggest Test batting score - A: 157; B: 207; C: 257; or D: 307?

930. In what year was Wasim Akram named as Wisden Cricketer of the Year?

INDIA

931. What words are displayed on the Indian badge by the national cricket team?

932. In what century was cricket first played in India?

933. In what city is the Feroz Shah Kotla Test stadium?

934. Who was appointed coach of the Indian national cricket team in November 2007?

935. Which Indian batsman has the most national achievements?

936. Which Indian bowler is one of the elite group of bowlers who have taken 500 wickets?

937. Indian players Pankaj Roy and Vinoo Mankad set the record for a first wicket partnership of what - A: 213; B: 313; C: 413; or D: 513?

938. Against which nation did India play its first ever Test match?

939. Who are the four bowlers known as the Indian Spin Quartet?

940. Against which nation did India record its first Test victory in Madras in 1952?

ONE DAY INTERNATIONALS - 3

941. Which English opening batsman faced the first ever One Day International delivery from Graham McKenzie of Australia?

942. Which English batsman set a record for the highest One Day International score for his nation, 167 not out against Australia in 1993?

943. Who scored the first ever One Day International century for England against Australia at Old Trafford in 1972?

944. Who was the first bowler to take five wickets in a One Day International for Australia against Pakistan in 1975?

945. Who set the highest One Day International batting total for India against Zimbabwe (175 not out) in 1983?

946. Which two Australian batsmen set the highest opening partnership record in a One Day International against India (212 in 1986/87)?

947. Which one of the following nations has played in a One Day International - A: Iraq; B: Palestine; C: Egypt; or D: United Arab Emirates?

948. In what nation was the first European Cricket Championship staged in 1996?

949. As of 2007, three nations have each won the European Cricket Championship twice - England, Ireland and who else?

950. True or false: France won the European Cricket Division Two title in 2004?

BARRY RICHARDS

951. In what year was Barry Richards born - A: 1943; B: 1944; C: 1945; or D: 1946?

952. Where was Barry Richards born?

953. What was the first County Cricket Club to employ Barry Richards' services?

954. Against which nation did Barry Richards make his Test debut in 1970?

955. What was Barry Richards' top Test score - A: 80; B: 100; C: 120; or D: 140?

956. In what year was Barry Richards named as Wisden Cricketer of the Year?

957. In 1973 Barry Richards walked out to open an innings with Hampshire in a John Player League match. Who was his batting partner?

958. For which Australian club was Barry Richards playing when he scored 325 against Western Australia in the 1970/71 season?

959. In what season did Barry Richards play in his last first class match?

960. Of which County Cricket Club is Barry Richards the President?

SIR FRANK WORRELL

961. What was Frank Worrell's full name?

962. By what nickname was Frank Worrell sometimes known?

963. Frank Worrell is the only batsman to have been involved in what cricketing record?

964. In what decade was Frank Worrell born?

965. In what year did Frank Worrell make his Test debut?

966. In what year was Frank Worrell knighted for services to cricket?

967. In what year was Frank Worrell named Wisden Cricketer of the Year?

968. In what year did Frank Worrell play his last Test match?

969. What was Frank Worrell's top Test score - A: 261; B: 271; C: 281; or D: 291?

970. In what year did Frank Worrell sadly pass away?

BANGLADESH

971. By what other name is the Bangladesh team known?

972. Who was the Bangladesh captain in 2007?

973. Against which nation did Bangladesh play its first One Day International match in 1986?

974. Which nation was the first to be defeated by Bangladesh in a Test match in 2005?

975. In June 2005, Bangladesh caused an upset by defeating which nation in a One Day International?

976. Bangladesh achieved its highest One Day International score of 301 for 7 against which nation in 2006?

977. Which Bangladesh bowler had taken the most test wickets for his nation as of 2007?

978. Which Bangladesh bowler took figures of 12 for 200 against Zimbabwe in 2005?

979. Which Bangladesh batsman has scored the most half-centuries as of 2007?

980. Who was the first Bangladesh captain at Test level?

YORKSHIRE

981. In what year was Yorkshire County Cricket Club formed?

982. What is Yorkshire's One Day name?

983. Who was the Yorkshire captain in 2007?

984. With which county did Yorkshire share the County Championship in 1949?

985. As of 2007, what year did Yorkshire last win the County Championship?

986. In what year did Yorkshire win the Benson and Hedges Cup?

987. Who was the Yorkshire coach in 2007?

988. Other than Headlingley, where does Yorkshire play a significant number of its home games?

989. Which current football ground was Yorkshire Cricket Club's first home?

990. For how many consecutive years did Yorkshire win the County Championship in the 1920s?

TEST CRICKET - 2

991. Which bowler once took 49 wickets in one Test series -
A: Harold Larwood; B: Jim Laker; C: Richie Benaud; or
D: Sydney Barnes?

992. Charles Bannerman scored the first ever Test century,
but in what year was he born - A: 1841; B: 1851; C:
1861; or D: 1871?

993. Which nation set a highest fourth innings record when
it scored 406 for 4 against the West Indies in 1975/76?

994. The longest Test match in history was recorded as
being 32 hours and 17 minutes long. The six day
match at The Oval between England and Australia was
drawn, but in what year was it played?

995. The only pair of batsmen to bat throughout two
consecutive days of Test cricket is Frank Worrell and
who else in 1960?

996. In 2005, which series was controversially granted Test
status by the ICC?

997. How long is a lunch break in Test cricket?

998. In what year was the last ever 'Timeless Test' match
played (a match played under no limitation of time)?

999. What is the highest number of bowlers to be used in a
Test match - A: 14; B: 16; C: 18; or D: 20?

1000. Which Indian bowler got ten wickets in an innings in a
Test match against Pakistan in Delhi in 1998/99?

ANSWERS

DICKIE BIRD

1.   Harold Dennis Bird

2.   Barnsley

3.   Leicestershire

4.   1964 (Leicestershire versus Essex)

5.   1973 (England versus New Zealand at Headingley)

6.   India and England

7.   Michael Parkinson

8.   MBE

9.   1933

10.   3 (1975, 1979 and 1983)

GROUNDS

11.   Headingley, Leeds

12.   Edgebaston

13.   Old Trafford

14.   County Ground (Riverside) Durham

15.   Sophia Gardens

16.   Mote Park, Maidstone, Kent CCC

17.   Rose Bowl, Southampton, Hampshire CCC

18.   Grace Road, Leicester, Leicestershire CCC

19.   Hove County Cricket Ground, Sussex CCC

20.   Valentines Park

BRIAN LARA

21.   The Prince

22.   1969

23.   1990 (versus Pakistan)

24.   Warwickshire

25.   Trinidad and Tobago

26.   9

27.   Pakistan in 2006

28.   Kevin Pietersen

29.   Mumbai Champs

30.   Australia in Sydney

NICKNAMES

31.	Phil Tufnell	The Cat
32.	Harold Bird	Dickie
33.	Shaun Udal	Shaggy
34.	Andrew Flintoff	Freddie
35.	Kevin Pietersen	KP
36.	Ian Botham	Beefy
37.	Graham Gooch	Zap
38.	Henry Blofield	Blowers
39.	Michael Atherton	Athers
40.	Nassar Hussain	Nass

THE WETHERALL AWARD

41.	2004	Robert Croft (Glamorgan)
42.	2002	Darren Maddy (Leicestershire)
43.	2000	Martin Bicknell (Surrey)
44.	1998	Gavin Hamilton (Yorkshire)
45.	1996	Phil Simmons (Leicestershire)
46.	1994	Franklyn Stephenson (Sussex)
47.	1992	Chris Lewis (Nottinghamshire)
48.	1990	Malcolm Marshall (Hampshire)
49.	1988	Franklyn Stephenson (Nottinghamshire)
50.	1986	Richard Hadlee (Nottinghamshire)

MIKE ATHERTON

51. 1968
52. Lancashire
53. Cockroach
54. Australia
55. 1989
56. Right-arm leg spin
57. India (in 1990)
58. 2001 (versus Australia)
59. His back
60. Opening Up

ONE DAY INTERNATIONALS - 1

61. 50
62. 1971
63. Australia and England
64. Pakistan
65. 21
66. Bangladesh
67. Sri Lanka
68. Saeed Anwar (194 runs versus India, 1996/79)
69. Wasim Akram (Pakistan)
70. Chaminda Vaas

ESSEX

71. Graham Gooch
72. D: 1876
73. Essex Eagles
74. Chelmsford
75. Peter Smith
76. 1979

77.   Mark Pettini

78.   1994.

79.   1986

80.   Danish Kaneria

SHANE WARNE

81.   Shane Keith Warne

82.   Victoria

83.   1992 (versus India)

84.   Andrew Strauss

85.   2004

86.   Muttiah Muralitharan of Pakistan

87.   Ravi Shastri

88.   23

89.   Right-arm leg break

90.   Alec Stewart

TEST CRICKET - 1

91.   1877

92.   England, Australia and South Africa

93.   England, Australia, South Africa, India, West Indies, New
       Zealand, Pakistan, Sri Lanka, Zimbabwe and Bangladesh

94.   1970

95.   1920s (1928)

96.   C: 2

97.   Lords

98.   80 overs

99.   West Indies (Georgetown 1970/71 until Bridgetown 1972/73)

100.   England versus Australia, The Oval, 1938

GRAHAM GOOCH

101.   1991

102.   1975 (versus Australia)

103.   Alan

104.   Western Province

105.   1995 (versus Australia)

106.   Leytonstone

107.   1981

108.   1988

109.   West Indies

110.   C: 23

AUSTRALIA

111.   Tim Nielsen

112.   Adam Gilchrist

113.   A: Charles Bannerman

114.   Steve Waugh

115.   South Africa

116.   Allan Border

117.   Matthew Hayden

118.   Glenn McGrath

119.   Mark Waugh

120.   'Under the Southern Cross I Stand'

CRICKET RULES

121.   Bat, bowl, act as captain or keep wicket

122.   Between 22.4cm and 22.9cm

123.   22 yards

124.   28 inches

125.   When the bowler begins his run-up

126.   3 minutes

127. One Day Internationals and Test Internationals only

128. The batting side keeps any penalty runs (such as no-balls and wides) and scores the higher of six runs plus the number of runs actually made

129. Just the batting team's score

130. No. But the bowler can be charged with misconduct by the match referee

ALEC STEWART

131. 1963

132. Surrey

133. Chelsea

134. Mark Butcher

135. 1993

136. West Indies

137. Pakistan

138. 1998

139. D: 3

140. Micky Stewart

MUTTIAH MURALITHARAN

141. 1972

142. Right-arm off break

143. Craig McDermott

144. Khaled Mashud

145. Lancashire

146. India

147. Tamil Union Cricket and Athletic Club

148. Paul Collingwood

149. Ben Hollioak

150. Kandy

UMPIRES

151. Steve Bucknor

152. Sahkoor Rana

153. David Shepherd

154. Darrell Hair

155. David Constant

156. Asoko De Silva

157. Rudi Koertzen

158. Srinivas Venkataraghavan

159. Peter Willey

160. Billy Doctrove

ENGLAND

161. Wales

162. Peter Moores

163. 3 (1979, 1987 and 1992)

164. Len Hutton

165. Wally Hammond, Geoff Boycott and Colin Cowdrey

166. W.G. Grace

167. Alec Stewart

168. Ian Botham

169. Nasser Hussain (56 matches)

170. Robin Smith

ANDREW FLINTOFF

171. Preston

172. B: Because his name is similar to that of cartoon character Fred Flintstone

173. 1998

174. South Africa

175. 11

176.   His ankle

177.   Alex Tudor

178.   2006

179.   Bat

180.   Rachael Woods

RECORDS

181.   India

182.   Victoria

183.   Ravi Shastri

184.   Brian Lara

185.   Don Bradman

186.   Wilfred Rhodes (1898 to 1930)

187.   Frank Woolley (58,959 runs, 2,066 wickets)

188.   1

189.   1986/87

190.   New Zealand

NORTHAMPTONSHIRE

191.   Northants Steelbacks

192.   Hampshire

193.   David Sales

194.   Never

195.   1878

196.   David Capel

197.   1980

198.   Nottinghamshire

199.   Mike Hussey

200.   2000

CRICKET HISTORY

201. 16th century (approximately 1550)

202. 1744

203. A: Along the ground

204. C: 1787

205. The Napoleonic Wars

206. C: Canada and the USA

207. B: 1890

208. D: 1940s

209. B: 1977

210. 2004

GEOFFREY BOYCOTT

211. 1940

212. Northern Transvaal

213. 1964

214. Graham Gooch

215. B: 7

216. 1982 (January)

217. Ian Botham

218. India

219. Boycs

220. 1965

DARREN GOUGH

221. Monk Bretton, near Barnsley

222. Essex

223. 8

224. New Zealand

225. 1994

226. Dazzler

227. 2003

228. Lilia Kopylova

229. Pakistan

230. A: 229

WORLD CUP 2007 - 1

231. Australia, England, New Zealand, South Africa, West Indies, Bangladesh, India, Pakistan, Sri Lanka, Zimbabwe, Bermuda, Canada, Kenya, Ireland, Netherlands and Scotland

232. Glenn McGrath (Australia)

233. Bob Woolmer

234. Scotland

235. Bermuda

236. Canada and Kenya

237. Australia, Sri Lanka, New Zealand and South Africa

238. Matthew Hayden

239. Paul Collingwood

240. Herschelle Gibbs

GRAHAM THORPE

241. 1969

242. Surrey

243. Kevin Pietersen

244. 1993

245. 2006

246. Bangladesh

247. Stumpy

248. Paul

249. 1988

250. He only hit one boundary

SIR DONALD BRADMAN

251. 1908

252. The Don

253. 99.94%

254. South Australia or New South Wales

255. Cootamundra

256. RAAF (Royal Australian Air Force)

257. 1947

258. Stockbroker

259. A: 29

260. 2001 (aged 92)

SIR GARFIELD SOBERS

261. Barbados

262. Nottinghamshire

263. 1954

264. 1974

265. Glamorgan

266. Bonaventure and the Flashing Blade

267. 1975

268. C: 57.78

269. D: 235

270. Malcolm Nash

CRICKET ON TV AND IN FILM

271. 1984

272. A: 1938

273. Peter Davison

274. Brian Johnstone

275. Kerry Packer

276. 1994

277.   1998

278.   *The Final Test*

279.   *Playing Away*

280.   1960

SIR VIV RICHARDS

281.   Isaac Vivian Alexander

282.   Master Blaster

283.   Glamorgan

284.   1974

285.   3 (1975, 1979 and 1987)

286.   C: 32

287.   1983

288.   1977

289.   1974

290.   Neena Gupta

NEIL FOSTER

291.   1962

292.   29

293.   New Zealand

294.   True

295.   Right-arm fast bowler

296.   1993

297.   1987

298.   446

299.   39 (versus Australia)

300.   Essex

WORLD CUP 2003

301.   South Africa

302.   *Zimbabwe*

303.   *Sri Lanka*

304.   *India*

305.   *Shane Warne*

306.   *Sachin Tendulkar (India)*

307.   *Chaminda Vaas*

308.   *Bangladesh*

309.   *Ricky Ponting (of Australia, 140 not out)*

310.   *David Shepherd*

SIR JACK HOBBS

311.   *Surrey*

312.   *1900s (1908)*

313.   *False. He was the oldest of 12 children*

314.   *C: 199*

315.   *John Berry Hobbs*

316.   *Herbert Sutcliffe*

317.   *W.G. Grace*

318.   *Air Mechanic for the Royal Flying Corps*

319.   *1950s (1953)*

320.   *Cricket journalist*

SIR IAN BOTHAM

321.   *Hampshire*

322.   *Queensland*

323.   *1977 (versus Australia)*

324.   *Kathy*

325.   *Somerset, Worcestershire and Durham*

326.   *B: 4*

327.   *His friends Joel Garner and Viv Richards had been sacked from the club*

328. A: 0

329. Pakistan

330. 1985

SOUTH AFRICA

331. Port Elizabeth

332. Graeme Smith

333. The Proteas

334. India

335. Kepler Wessels

336. Mickey Arthur

337. 1998

338. Shaun Pollock

339. Australia

340. 1998

DENNIS LILLEE

341. 1940s (1949)

342. B: 1

343. Western Australia

344. 1970/71

345. Terry Alderman

346. Rod Marsh

347. Javed Miandad

348. Tasmania

349. B: 7

350. 1979 at the WACA against England

ASHES HISTORY

351. 2005   2-1

352. 2001   1-4

353.	1993	1-4
354.	1985	3-1
355.	1975	0-1
356.	1961	1-2
357.	1953	1-0
358.	1948	0-4
359.	1930	1-2
360.	1909	1-2

WORLD CUP 2007 - 2

361. Scotland

362. South Africa (294)

363. Bermuda

364. Glenn McGrath (Australia)

365. Matthew Hayden

366. Ricky Ponting (113 for Australia, versus Scotland)

367. Sri Lanka

368. Ireland

369. Matthew Hayden

370. New Zealand

SACHIN TENDULKAR

371. The Little Master

372. D: Ramesh

373. 1989

374. 10

375. Bombay

376. Yorkshire

377. Mike Denness

378. Kris Srikkanth

379. The death of his father

380.   *1973*

WORLD CUP 1999

381.   *Sachin Tendulkar (140, versus Kenya)*

382.   *New Zealand and Pakistan*

383.   *Bangladesh*

384.   *Pakistan*

385.   *The match was tied*

386.   *Shane Warne*

387.   *Lance Klusener of South Africa*

388.   *Wajahatullah Wasti*

389.   *Rahul Dravid (461 runs)*

390.   *Geoff Allott (20 wickets)*

WINNERS OF THE HONG KONG SIXES

391.	2005	India
392.	2004	England
393.	2003	England
394.	2002	Pakistan
395.	2001	Pakistan
396.	1997	Pakistan
397.	1996	South Indies
398.	1995	South Africa
399.	1994	England
400.	1993	England

SIR CLYDE WALCOTT

401.   *1940s (1948)*

402.   *West Indies*

403.   *Everton Weekes and Frank Worrell*

404.   *ICC*

405. *False. Sir Clyde said that Theo Walcott was definitely not a*
     relative
406. *1960s (1960)*
407. *A: 220*
408. *B: 11*
409. *Wicketkeeper*
410. *1958*

CRICKET IN THE USA

411. *George Washington*
412. *New York*
413. *Baseball*
414. *1960s (1965)*
415. *2004*
416. *Steve Massiah*
417. *For failing to meet the agreed and subsequently extended*
     deadlines for the adoption of its constitution and the holding of
     elections
418. *Bart King*
419. *True*
420. *Richard Staple*

IMRAN KHAN

421. *Imran Khan Niazi*
422. *1952 (25 November)*
423. *Punjab*
424. *1971*
425. *England*
426. *Worcestershire*
427. *Sussex*
428. *1992*

429. *Politics*

430. *1983*

PAKISTAN

431. *1952*

432. *India*

433. *Shoaib Malik*

434. *India*

435. *Geoff Lawson*

436. *2000*

437. *False. It has won more than it has lost*

438. *True*

439. *5 (1979, 1983 and 1987 semi-finalist; 1992 champion; 1999 runner-up)*

440. *Karachi and Lahore.*

MICHAEL VAUGHAN

441. *Paul*

442. *Virgil (sometimes known as Vaughany and Frankie)*

443. *1993*

444. *1999*

445. *South Africa*

446. *2003*

447. *2001*

448. *B: 6*

449. *West Indies*

450. *Manchester*

WORLD CUP 1987

451. *Allan Border*

452. *India and Pakistan*

453.   *Graham Gooch (England)*

454.   *Craig McDermott (Australia)*

455.   *Pakistan*

456.   *Javed Miandad (103 runs)*

457.   *Graham Gooch*

458.   *David Boon*

459.   *Ram Gupta or Mahboob Shah*

460.   *Reliance*

JIM LAKER

461.   *1920s (1922)*

462.   *Surrey and Essex*

463.   *1952*

464.   *West Indies*

465.   *1956*

466.   *Old Trafford, Manchester*

467.   *1959*

468.   *D: 90*

469.   *He was a cricket commentator for BBC television*

470.   *1986 (23 April)*

COUNTRY CRICKET - 1

471.   *Gloucestershire, Kent, Lancashire, Middlesex, Nottinghamshire, Surrey, Sussex and Yorkshire*

472.   *Durham*

473.   *Somerset*

474.   *2000*

475.   *Surrey*

476.   *Yorkshire*

477.   *Durham, Gloucestershire, Northamptonshire and Somerset*

478.   *Yorkshire (30 as of 2007)*

479. *Derbyshire*

480. *Schweppes*

CURTLY AMBROSE

481. *1963*

482. *Little Bird*

483. *Antigua*

484. *1988*

485. *Northamptonshire*

486. *Pakistan*

487. *C: 405*

488. *True*

489. *2000 (versus England)*

490. *Richie Richardson*

MIKE BREARLEY

491. *John*

492. *A: 0*

493. *1976*

494. *West Indies*

495. *Middlesex*

496. *MCC*

497. *Harrow, Middlesex*

498. *1940s (28 April 1942)*

499. *Ian Botham*

500. *OBE*

MORE ON BEEFY

501. *1981*

502. *1978*

503. *Smoking cannabis*

504. *Crystal Palace*

505. *Central defender*

506. *1980*

507. *Yeovil Town*

508. *John O'Groats to Land's End*

509. *2007*

510. *Leukaemia Research*

SOMERSET

511. *12 times*

512. *1875*

513. *Jack White*

514. *Harold Gimblett*

515. *Somerset Sabres*

516. *County Cricket Ground, Taunton*

517. *1979*

518. *Middlesex*

519. *Justin Langer*

520. *2005*

WORLD CUP 1992

521. *Australia*

522. *Martin Crowe (New Zealand)*

523. *New Zealand*

524. *Wasim Akram (Pakistan)*

525. *Ian Botham*

526. *South Africa*

527. *Sri Lanka (313 for 7)*

528. *David Boon (versus New Zealand and the West Indies)*

529. *Imran Khan*

530. *England*

DURHAM

531.   1882

532.   Dale Benkenstein

533.   15,000

534.   Warwickshire

535.   Yellow cross on a blue background. (Bonus if four lions in each corner are mentioned)

536.   Geoff Cook

537.   Zimbabwe

538.   Friends Provident Trophy

539.   David Boon

540.   Durham Dynamos

WALLY HAMMOND

541.   1900s (1903)

542.   Gloucestershire

543.   Dover, Kent

544.   C: 1927

545.   Slip

546.   False. He scored 336 not out

547.   So he could captain England. The position was barred to professionals until Len Hutton took charge

548.   B: 1947

549.   A: 83

550.   1960s (1 July 1965)

YOUNG CRICKETER OF THE YEAR

551.   1979   Paul Parker

552.   1969   Alan Ward

553.   1957   Micky Stewart

554.   1996   Chris Silverwood

555.	2001	Owais Shah
556.	2005	Alastair Cook
557.	1998	Andrew Flintoff
558.	1983	Neil Foster
559.	1990	Michael Atherton
560.	1981	Mike Gatting

SRI LANKA

561.	Ceylon
562.	Kenya
563.	Muttiah Muralitharan
564.	Sanath Jayasuriya
565.	Arjuna Ranatunga
566.	England (1982)
567.	Mahela Jayawardene
568.	Trevor Bayliss
569.	2006
570.	Aravinda De Silva

RICHIE BENAUD

571.	1930s (6 October 1930)
572.	New South Wales
573.	1952
574.	West Indies
575.	South Africa
576.	True
577.	1964
578.	"Good morning everyone"
579.	John
580.	My Spin on Cricket

MIKE GATTING

581. 1957 (6 June)

582. Brighton and Hove Albion

583. William

584. Middlesex

585. 1978

586. Pakistan

587. John Emburey

588. B: 207

589. 1995

590. 1998

SUNIL GAVASKAR

591. 1940s (1949)

592. Sachin Tendulkar

593. 1971

594. A: 236

595. Sunny

596. B: 1

597. West Indies

598. Kapil Dev

599. Pakistan

600. Rohan Gavaskar

THE LORDS TAVERNERS

601. 1950s (1950)

602. Sir John Mills

603. 1952

604. One Day or Sunday cricket

605. HRH The Duke of Edinburgh

606. Youth cricket

607.   *Tim Rice*

608.   *The Buccaneers*

609.   *800*

610.   *Bill Tidy*

BASIL D'OLIVEIRA

611.   *1930s (4 October 1931)*

612.   *Cape Town, South Africa*

613.   *Worcestershire*

614.   *1966*

615.   *Dolly*

616.   *Ivan D'Oliveira*

617.   *John Arlott*

618.   *1969*

619.   *1972*

620.   *1980*

MCC

621.   *Marylebone Cricket Club*

622.   *A: 1787*

623.   *C: Thomas Lord*

624.   *Egg and bacon (yellow and red)*

625.   *Her Majesty the Queen*

626.   *The Conduit Club*

627.   *Dorset Square*

628.   *St Johns Wood Road*

629.   *1814*

630.   *Nursery End*

WORLD CUP 1996

631.   Wills

632.   India, Pakistan and Sri Lanka

633.   Sanath Jayasuriya (Sri Lanka)

634.   Sachin Tendulkar (India)

635.   Anil Kumble (India)

636.   United Arab Emirates or Netherlands

637.   Nathan Astle

638.   The match referee awarded the game to Sri Lanka when rioting
        India fans held it up

639.   Aravinda de Silva (Sri Lanka)

640.   Australia

HAT-TRICKS

641.   South Africa

642.   Wasim Akram

643.   Damien Fleming

644.   Lasith Malinga (28 March 2007, for Sri Lanka, versus South
        Africa)

645.   Devon Malcolm

646.   Darren Gough

647.   West Indies

648.   Courtney Walsh

649.   Matthew Hoggard

650.   James Anderson

BODYLINE

651.   C: 1932/33

652.   Fast Leg Theory

653.   Douglas Jardine

654.   Harold Larwood, Bill Bowes and Bill Voce

655. **Bill Woodfull**

656. **4-1**

657. **Bert Oldfield**

658. **West Indies**

659. **1935**

660. **C: Hugh Buggy (although Jack Worrall tried to take credit for it)**

ONE DAY INTERNATIONALS - 2

661. **Rudi Koertzen**

662. **Mohammad Azharuddin**

663. **Adam Gilchrist**

664. **Bangladesh**

665. **Joel Garner (West Indies)**

666. **Darren Gough**

667. **Sanath Jayasuriya and Sachin Tendulkar**

668. **Andrew Flintoff**

669. **Matthew Hayden (Australia)**

670. **Garry Sobers**

NOTTINGHAMSHIRE

671. **Nottinghamshire Outlaws**

672. **A: 1841**

673. **5 (1907, 1929, 1981, 1987 and 2005)**

674. **1989**

675. **Chris Read**

676. **George Gunn**

677. **Thomas Waas**

678. **Essex**

679. **Richard Hadlee**

680. **Harold Larwood**

THE WEST INDIES

681. The Windies

682. India (in Bombay)

683. A tropical island with a wicket

684. David Moore

685. England

686. Jerome Taylor

687. Ramnaresh Sarwan

688. D: Queen's Park Oval, Port of Spain, Trinidad

689. Mike Findlay

690. 2004

SIR RICHARD HADLEE

691. 1951 (3 July)

692. Paddles

693. Pakistan

694. 1990

695. Right-arm fast

696. Canterbury

697. B: 151 not out

698. 1990

699. C: Tripping up on a run-up to bowl. New Zealand versus England at Lords, 1978. As he started to run in to bowl to Graham Gooch, he tripped over his feet and fell on his face. There were over 28,000 people in the ground and the match was being televised live

700. B: An autograph book containing thousands of cricketers' signatures

MIDDLESEX

701.   *Lords*

702.   *Middlesex Crusaders*

703.   *1864*

704.   *Ed Smith*

705.   *Three cutlasses one above the other on a blue shield*

706.   *Fred Titmus*

707.   *Denis Compton (along with his brother Leslie)*

708.   *12 (1903, 1920, 1921, 1947, 1976, 1980, 1982, 1985, 1990, 1993; shared in 1949 and 1977)*

709.   *1983*

710.   *John Emburey*

WORLD CUP 1983

711.   *David Gower (England, 384 runs)*

712.   *Allan Lamb*

713.   *India*

714.   *Roger Binny*

715.   *Australia*

716.   *It was damaged during a violent rampage at the Indian cricket board's headquarters, allegedly carried out by members of the Hindu nationalist group Shiv Sena*

717.   *Because of industrial action at the BBC*

718.   *Pakistan*

719.   *27*

720.   *Barrie Mayer*

SUSSEX

721.   *1836*

722.   *Sussex Sharks*

723.   *Chris Adams*

724. Hove

725. 2003

726. 3 (2003, 2006 and 2007)

727. 2001

728. Murray Goodwin

729. The martlet (bird with no legs)

730. John Langridge

CRICKETING TERMS - 1

731. Chinaman

732. Nightwatchman

733. Offside

734. Playing on

735. Plumb

736. Sledging

737. Yorker

738. Diamond duck

739. Daisy cutter

740. Duckworth-Lewis method

WORLD TWENTY20

741. South Africa

742. Shahid Afridi (Pakistan)

743. Matthew Hayden (Australia)

744. Umar Gul (Pakistan)

745. Chris Gayle

746. Zimbabwe

747. Australia and New Zealand

748. Mark Benson

749. Gautam Gambhir (India, 75)

750. Brett Lee

LADIES CRICKET

751.   Betty Archdale

752.   Charlotte Edwards

753.   Twice (1973 and 1993)

754.   Pakistan

755.   Rachael Heyhoe-Flint

756.   Myrtle Maclagan

757.   Mary Duggan

758.   Ireland

759.   B: 1745

760.   White Heather Club (formed in 1887)

DAVID GOWER

761.   1957 (1 April)

762.   Tunbridge Wells, Kent

763.   Lubo, Lu or Stoat

764.   Leicestershire and Hampshire

765.   Pakistan

766.   B: 1

767.   Bob Willis

768.   True

769.   1992

770.   They Think It's All Over

SURREY

771.   1845

772.   Surrey Brown Caps

773.   Mark Butcher

774.   The Oval

775.   Chocolate brown and silver

776.   The Prince of Wales feathers

777. *2003*

778. *Lancashire*

779. *Gloucestershre*

780. *Mark Ramprakash*

WORLD CUP 1979

781. *Prudential*

782. *England*

783. *Canada*

784. *Gordon Greenidge (253 runs)*

785. *Mike Hendrick (10 wickets)*

786. *Clive Lloyd*

787. *England (versus Canada)*

788. *Kim Hughes*

789. *Viv Richards (West Indies)*

790. *New Zealand*

MALCOLM MARSHALL

791. *1950s (18 April 1958)*

792. *Hampshire*

793. *C: 92*

794. *Denzil*

795. *India*

796. *1980*

797. *1992 (versus New Zealand)*

798. *C: 376*

799. *1999*

800. *Bridgetown*

FRED TRUEMAN

801. C: Sewards

802. 1930s (6 February 1931)

803. Derbyshire

804. Indoor League

805. *Dad's Army*

806. *Hitchhiker's Guide to the Galaxy*

807. 1952 (versus India)

808. 1965 (versus New Zealand)

809. Raquel Welch

810. 2006

KENT

811. St Lawrence Ground

812. Kent Spitfires

813. 1806

814. 2007

815. 1906

816. Rob Key

817. Middlesex

818. Frank Woolley (47,868 runs)

819. Derek Underwood

820. 1973

BRIAN JOHNSTONE

821. C: He was a Governor of the Bank of England

822. False

823. Johnners

824. Military Cross

825. India

826. D: *Come Dancing*

827.   Johnstone said, "The bowler's Holding, the batsman's Willey"

828.   Test Match Special

829.   The Bearded Wonder

830.   1994

CLIVE LLOYD

831.   1944 (31 August)

832.   British Guiana (now known as Guyana)

833.   Big C or Hubert

834.   Lance Gibbs

835.   1966

836.   D: 10

837.   1992 (South Africa versus India at Durban)

838.   1984

839.   1971

840.   Lancashire

CRICKETING TERMS - 2

841.   Googly

842.   Gully

843.   Long hop

844.   Maiden over

845.   Brace

846.   Perfume ball

847.   Bunsen (from the rhyming slang: 'Bunsen Burner' meaning 'Turner')

848.   Cow shot

849.   Doosra (the finger spin equivalent of the googly, in that it turns the 'wrong way'; from the Hindi or Urdu for second or other)

850.   Featherbed

WORLD CUP 1975

851. England, New Zealand, India, East Africa, West Indies, Australia, Pakistan and Sri Lanka

852. England

853. Glenn Turner (New Zealand)

854. Gary Gilmour (Australia)

855. Dennis Amiss (137 runs)

856. Clive Lloyd

857. Viv Richards

858. Headingley, Leeds

859. Tom Spencer

860. Tony Greig

NEW ZEALAND

861. New Zealand Black Caps

862. 1998

863. Zimbabwe (59 and 99 all out)

864. Australia

865. Lance and Chris Cairns

866. Lou Vincent (172 runs)

867. Nathan Astle

868. Geoff Allott

869. Danny Morrison (24 Test ducks)

870. Richard Collinge

BISHAN BEDI

871. 1940s (25 September 1946)

872. Punjab

873. Northamptonshire

874. 1966 (31 December)

875. *A: Basil Butcher*

876. *1974*

877. *B: 50*

878. *D: 266*

879. *1979*

880. *Muttiah Muralitharan*

WARWICKSHIRE

881. *1882*

882. *Warwickshire Bears*

883. *Dennis Amiss*

884. *6 (1911, 1951, 1972, 1994, 1995 and 2004)*

885. *Durham*

886. *Brian Lara*

887. *Jack Bannister*

888. *Hampshire (Hampshire posted 521 in their second innings and bowled out Warwickshire, who needed 314 to win, for 158)*

889. *True*

890. *Ashley Giles*

MIKE PROCTER

891. *1940s (15 September 1946)*

892. *Prock or Procky*

893. *Durban, Natal (South Africa)*

894. *Gloucestershire*

895. *1967*

896. *Australia*

897. *1970*

898. *Northamptonshire*

899. *2002 (Pakistan v New Zealand at Lahore, May 1-3)*

9000.   *Woodrow Procter (father), Anthony Procter (brother) or*

            Andrew Procter (cousin)

STEVE WAUGH

901.   *1965*

902.   *Tugga or Ice Man*

903.   *Kent*

904.   *1985*

905.   *New South Wales*

906.   *2004 (He was honoured by his nation for his sporting*

            achievements and his charity work)

907.   *2004 (versus India)*

908.   *Right-arm medium*

909.   *C: 3*

910.   *B: 10,927*

COUNTY CRICKET - 2

911.   *Mike Procter*

912.   *Lancashire*

913.   *Warwickshire*

914.   *Nottinghamshire*

915.   *B: 57 (Reverend Reginald Moss, who was 57 years and 89 days*

            old when he played for Worcestershire against

            Gloucestershire, 23-26 May 1925)

916.   *Sussex (between 1954 and 1969)*

917.   *Glamorgan*

918.   *Yorkshire*

919.   *Northamptonshire*

920.   *Glamorgan*

WASIM AKRAM

921. 1966

922. The Sultan of Swing

923. Lancashire

924. Hampshire

925. 1985

926. Brian Lara

927. 2002 (versus Bangladesh)

928. D: 502

929. C: 257 (not out)

930. 1993

INDIA

931. Board of Control for Cricket in India

932. 18th (early 1700s)

933. Delhi

934. Gary Kirsten

935. Sachin Tendulkar

936. Anil Kumble

937. C: 413

938. England (Lords, June 1932)

939. Erapalli Prasanna, Srinivas Venkataraghavan, Bhagwat Chandrasekhar and Bishen Singh Bedi

940. England

ONE DAY INTERNATIONALS - 3

941. Geoffrey Boycott

942. Robin Smith

943. Dennis Amiss

944. Dennis Lillee

945. Kapil Dev

946.   *Geoff Marsh and David Boon*

947.   *D: United Arab Emirates*

948.   *Denmark*

949.   *Netherlands*

950.   *False. Italy won and France was runner-up*

BARRY RICHARDS

951.   *C: 1945.*

952.   *Durban, South Africa*

953.   *Gloucestershire*

954.   *Australia*

955.   *D: 140*

956.   *1969*

957.   *Gordon Greenidge*

958.   *South Australia*

959.   *1982/83*

960.   *Hampshire*

SIR FRANK WORRELL

961.   *Frank Mortimer Maglinne Worrell*

962.   *Tae*

963.   *He is the only batsman to have been involved in two 500-run partnerships in first class cricket*

964.   *1920s (1 August 1924)*

965.   *1948*

966.   *1964*

967.   *1951*

968.   *1963*

969.   *A: 261*

970.   *1967 (13 March)*

BANGLADESH

971.   *The Tigers*

972.   *Mohammad Ashraful*

973.   *Pakistan*

974.   *Zimbabwe*

975.   *Australia*

976.   *Kenya*

977.   *Mohammad Rafique*

978.   *Enamul Haque Jr*

979.   *Habibul Bashar*

980.   *Naimur Rahman*

YORKSHIRE

981.   *1863*

982.   *Yorkshire Phoenix*

983.   *Darren Gough*

984.   *Middlesex*

985.   *2001*

986.   *1987*

987.   *Martyn Moxon*

988.   *North Marine Road, Scarborough*

989.   *Bramall Lane, Sheffield United FC*

990.   *4 (1922/25)*

TEST CRICKET - 2

991.   *D: Sydney Barnes (for England, versus South Africa, 1913/14)*

992.   *B: 1851*

993.   *India*

994.   *1975*

995.   *Garfield Sobers (versus England at the Kensington Oval)*

996.   *The six day Super Series between Australia and World XI*

997. *40 minutes*

998. *1939*

999. *D: 20 (South Africa versus England, January 1965, Cape Town)*

1000. *Anil Kumble*

WORKING FOR THE FUTURE OF SPORT

ABOUT
THE DICKIE BIRD FOUNDATION

The foundation was established by Dickie in March 2004, with the aim of helping disadvantaged young people, nationwide, to participate in sport.

Its objective is:
"To assist financially disadvantaged young people under 18 years of age to participate, to the best of their ability, in the sport of their choice irrespective of their social circumstances, culture or ethnicity and to ensure that, in doing so, they improve their chances both inside and outside sport."

It is our fervent hope that, through our efforts and the grants we make, more young people will be able to access sport and fulfill their ambitions as sportsmen whilst at the same time improving their prospects in life.

If you feel you are a young person (under 18) or somebody in your school, club, college or sports association who meets our criteria, please download an application form from our website. Every application will be given fair and equal consideration.

Les Smith, 47 Ripon Road, Earlsheaton,
Dewsbury, West Yorkshire, WF12 7LG
Email: info@thedickiebirdfoundation.org
Website: www.thedickiebirdfoundation.org

144

OTHER BOOKS BY CHRIS COWLIN:

The Gooners Quiz Book

Foreword by: Bob Wilson
ISBN: 1-904444-77-6   978-1-904444-77-0
Price: £8.99

Will you do the Gooners proud as you display an impressive knowledge of your favourite club, Arsenal, or will you instead prove yourself to be a complete goon, as trip over your own feet in search of the answers to the 1,000 cunning questions in this quiz book?

Covering every aspect of the club's history from players to managers and from national to international competitions since its foundation over a century ago, and with a fitting Foreword by former Scotland and Arsenal goalkeeping legend and TV presenter, Bob Wilson, this book will challenge Gooners fans of all ages as well as providing fascinating facts and figures both to enthral and to trigger fond memories and ardent discussions.

If you find yourself floundering, you can recover your dignity and find consolation in the fact that £1 from the sale of every book will go to the Willow Foundation, a charity founded by Bob and Megs Wilson and dedicated to arranging individually tailored 'Special Days' for seriously ill young adults.

The Official Aston Villa Quiz Book

Foreword by: Graham Taylor OBE
ISBN: 1-906358-05-2   978-1-906358-05-1
Price: £7.99

Will you be a roaring lion or a quivering mouse as you attempt to face the villains of this book, i.e. the 1,000 challenging quiz questions that will have your minds hopping through over a hundred years of Aston Villa's history at lightning pace?

No stone remains unturned in terms of question topics, from cherished players, memorable managers and thrilling competitions to opponents, transfers, nationalities and awards, interspersed with sneaky bits of trivia to test the knowledge of even the most ardent Villa aficionado.

With a fitting foreword by Graham Taylor OBE, this book is a veritable mine of interesting facts and figures and is guaranteed to spark fond memories of much-loved characters and enthralling matches, and no doubt even heated discussion, as fans pit their wits against family and friends.

OTHER BOOKS BY CHRIS COWLIN:

The Official Wolves Quiz Book
Foreword by: John Richards
ISBN: 1-904444-94-6   978-1-904444-94-7
Price: £7.99

You might think you know all there is to know about Wolves, but what if they're disguised in sheep's clothing and take the form of 1,000 tricky quiz questions that could give you a nasty bite? Your brains will certainly have to adopt the role of wanderer as you try to cast your minds back well over a century to the very beginning of the club's long history.

Questions cover every imaginable aspect of the club, from memorable managers and players, through transfer fees, opponents, scores and awards, to every competition you can think of, and they are sure to trigger vivid and treasured recollections of the colourful characters and nail-biting matches that have made the club what it is today.

With a fitting foreword by John Richards, this book is bursting at the seams with interesting facts and figures and is guaranteed to challenge even the most ardent fan as well as provide hours of entertainment for the whole family.

The Southend United Quiz Book
Foreword by: Frank Dudley
ISBN: 1-904444-91-1   978-1904444-91-6
Price: £5.99

Will you be a Shrimper with a record catch as you reel in the answers to the 800 tricky questions in this quiz book about Southend United Football Club, or will you be singing the Blues as you bemoan the one, or more, that got away?

Your knowledge about all aspects of the club since its formation will be tested to the limit, from memorable managers and players to transfer fees, opponents, scores, awards and all the unforgettable competitions and matches that have kept fans on the edge of their seats throughout the club's long history.

With a fitting foreword by Frank Dudley, this quiz book is brimming with interesting facts and figures and is guaranteed to provide hours of entertainment, reminiscing and discussion for fans of the club.

OTHER BOOKS BY CHRIS COWLIN:

The Official Carry On Quiz Book
Foreword by: Norman Hudis and Jacki Piper
ISBN: 1-904444-97-0   978-1-904444-97-8
Price: £7.99
Who can forget the cheeky humour, outrageous characters and slapstick comedy that have characterised the 'Carry On' films over the last fifty years? Well, don't lose your head if you discover that the 1,000 questions in this quiz book highlight a few holes in your memory and you end up in hospital screaming for the saucy nurse and ending up with the grumpy old matron!
Covering every aspect of the 'Carry On' genre – the movies, release dates, characters, the stars and their lives, debuts, and much more – this book will propel you on a whirlwind journey from the Wild West to the Khyber Pass and every conceivable location in between, hotfooting through a range of historical eras, and jumping between black-and-white and Technicolor worlds.
Even if you find you're cruising on rough waters, carry on regardless, make the most of the entertainment facilities, delve into the treasure trove of facts and figures, and allow your fond recollections to turn your frowns into the smiles and giggles that encapsulate the 'Carry On' ethos.

Celebrities' Favourite Football Teams
Foreword by: Sir Alex Ferguson CBE
ISBN: 1-904444-84-9   978-1904444-84-8
Price: £6.99
We all like to delve into the minds and lives of our beloved celebrity figures, but this fascinating read is not celebrity gossip, it comes straight from the horse's mouth to reveal all you ever wanted to know about celebrities' favourite football teams and players.
With a fitting Foreword by footballing legend Sir Alex Ferguson CBE, this book is a must-read for football fans who wish to know which celebrity is a fellow aficionado of their club, or perhaps a supporter of 'the enemy', as well as for the rest of the population, who just love to know what makes our celebrities tick.
And it is also a must-buy, as all royalties from the sale of this book will be donated to The Willow Foundation, a charity set up by the legendary Bob Wilson and his wife Megs in 1999 to enable seriously ill young adults to enjoy the treat of a 'Special Day' with family and friends.

OTHER BOOKS BY CHRIS COWLIN:

The Official Watford Football Club Quiz Book
Foreword by: Graham Taylor OBE
ISBN: 1-904444-85-7   978-1-904444-85-5
Price: £7.99
Be prepared to stir up a veritable hornets nest as you strive to meet the challenge of answering 1,000 testing questions about Watford Football Club. This quiz book certainly has the 'ouch' factor, guaranteeing that even the most ardent fan will get stung several times along the way.
Covering every subject imaginable about the Hornets, from players of old to the most recent Cup competitions, it not only contains a wealth of interesting facts and figures but also will stir up fond memories of all the great personalities and nail-biting matches that have helped to mould the Club throughout its long history.
With a fitting Foreword by legendary Watford Manager, Graham Taylor OBE, this book will provide hours of entertainment for the whole family who, whilst licking their wounds, can console themselves in the knowledge that £1 from the sale of each copy will be donated to the charity Sense, which helps deaf and blind people of all ages lead fuller and happier lives.

The Official Colchester United Quiz Book
Foreword by: Karl Duguid
ISBN: 1-904444-88-1   978-1904444-88-6
Price: £5.99
Question: How many U's are there in Colchester? Answer: One, of course - as all Colchester United fans ought to know. And, if that little teaser caught you out, then brace yourselves for 750 more tricky questions, relating to your favourite team, the U's.
Covering all aspects of the club, from players and managers to nationalities and every conceivable tournament, you will be required to U's your brainpower to its limit to come up with all the answers and amaze (or otherwise) your friends and family with the depth of your knowledge about the club.
With a fitting Foreword by Karl Duguid, this book will trigger recollections of favourite players past and present, nail-biting matches, and all the club's highs and lows over their long history. A veritable treasure trove of facts and figures is at your fingertips – enjoy!

OTHER BOOKS BY CHRIS COWLIN:

The Official Norwich City Quiz Book
Foreword by: Bryan Gunn
ISBN: 1-904444-80-6   978-1-904444-80-0
Price: £7.99

Will you be singing like a Canary as you fly with ease through this book's 1,000 challenging quiz questions about Norwich City Football Club, or will you have flown the Nest too soon and come crashing to the ground spitting feathers?

Covering all aspects of the club's history, including top goalscorers, transfers, managers, Cup competitions, League positions, awards, legendary players and nationalities, it will push to the limit even the most ardent aficionados' knowledge of their favourite team.

With a fitting foreword by the legendary Bryan Gunn, this book is guaranteed to trigger fond recollections of all the nail-biting matches and colourful characters that have shaped the club over the years, as well as providing a wealth of interesting facts and figures with which to impress your friends and family.

The British TV Sitcom Quiz Book
Foreword by: Brian Murphy
ISBN: 1-906358-20-6   978-1-906358-20-4
Price: £7.99

Television situation comedy classics have issued forth from the pens of genius writers and partnerships unabated for the last 50 years in Britain and, if you think you know all there is to know as an aficionado, you may find yourself laughing on the other side of your face as you attempt to conjure up the answers to the 1,000 testing quiz questions contained in this book.

All aspects of the genre are covered – the many series, the creators, the unforgettable, larger-than-life characters, and the wonderful actors and actresses that have made them come to life in comedies ranging from Hancock's Half Hour in the 1950s, through the innumerable greats that have graced every subsequent decade of the last century, to The Office of the new millennium – so even the most ardent sitcom fans will need their wits about them.

This book is as much a treasure trove of fascinating facts and figures as it is an entertaining quiz book for all the family, and it is sure to sort out the Victor Meldrews from the David Brents, stir up many fond memories, create plenty of smiles and oil a few chuckle muscles along the way.

OTHER BOOKS BY ADAM PEARSON:

The Official Southampton Quiz Book
Foreword by: Francis Benali
ISBN: 1-904444-67-9   978-1-904444-67-1
Price: £8.99
Here's a challenge for all you Southampton Football Club fans. Will you prove yourselves to be sinners as you are sent reeling by the 1,200 fiendish questions in this book, or will you emerge saints and be polishing your halos, as you gloat over how much you know about your favourite team?

Covering every possible aspect of the Saints' long history, including players, managers, opponents, scores, transfers, nationalities, seasons, League positions, Cup competitions, and much more, you'll be searching every corner of your brains to come up with the answers.

With a fitting foreword by Francis Benali, this tribute to the Saints will trigger fond recollections of all the nail-biting matches and unforgettable personalities that have left an imprint on the club's history, and it is as much a treasure trove of amazing and wide-ranging facts and figures as it is an entertaining quiz book.

The Official Leicester City Quiz Book
Foreword by: Tony Cottee
ISBN: 1-904444-86-5   978-1904444-86-2
Price: £7.99
Can you outfox your friends and family by answering the 1,000 cunning questions about Leicester City Football Club contained in this quiz book, or will you be like a rabbit caught in the headlights?

Questions cover all aspects of the club, from memorable managers and players to transfer fees, opponents and awards, and are sure to conjure up fond reminiscences of the colourful characters and nail-biting matches that have peppered the club's long history.

With a fitting foreword by Tony Cottee, this is as much a treasure trove of interesting facts and figures as it is a quiz book, and is guaranteed to provide hours of entertainment for young and old alike.